DRAWINGS

FROM THE COLLECTION OF

CURTIS O. BAER

DRAWINGS FROM THE COLLECTION OF CURTIS O. BAER

January 11   1958   February 25

THE FOGG ART MUSEUM

CAMBRIDGE · MASSACHUSETTS

The illustration on the cover is an enlarged
detail of Rembrandt's *The Matchmaker* (?), no. 29
in this catalogue

PRINTED IN THE UNITED STATES OF AMERICA

Design and letterpress by The Stinehour Press

Illustration by The Meriden Gravure Company

List of Illustrations

References are to catalogue listings and illustration numbers.

Acknowledgments

WE have called upon many of our colleagues, both here and abroad, for assistance in the fields of their special competence. All have responded with the most ready and generous help. Among them are Alfred H. Barr, K. G. Boon, Otto J. Brendel, Frederick B. Deknatel, Nancy E. Curtis, Herbert Dieckmann, Sydney J. Freedberg, Mme. René Jasinski, Mrs. Ruth Wedgwood Kennedy, Denis Mahon, Millard Meiss, Erwin Panofsky, E. K. J. Reznicek, Jakob Rosenberg, Eric Schroeder, Eduard Sekler, Seymour Slive, Wolfgang Stechow and Mrs. Dorothy Usher Wilson.

We have also been aided by both our former and present students. The following entries are, in fact, almost completely the work of our young colleagues: Nos. 52, 53, 54, 58, 59, 60, 61 by Richard S. Field; 48, 49 by Alain W. de Leiris; 17, 18, 56 by Svetlana E. Leontief; 5, 6, 7, 8, 38 by Mrs. Sylvia Perrera Massell; 12, 46, 47, 50, 55 by Emily S. Rauh; 51 by Theodore F. Reff.

Last but not least we are grateful to Mrs. Barbara A. Holleman, who has prepared the manuscript in its entirety.

Several references were so commonly used that it was decided not to give the full data each time. These are as follows:

Archives: Caisse Nationale des Monuments Historiques, Grand Palais, Cours la Reine (Porte F), Paris 8ᵉ, France.

Briquet: Briquet, C. M., *Les Filigranes*, Leipzig, von Karl W. Hiersemann, 1923, Vols. I, II, III and IV.

Gernsheim: Dr. Walter Gernsheim, Villa Corbinelli, Via Suor Maria Celeste 12, Florence, Italy.

L. No.: Lugt, Frits, *Les Marques de Collections de Dessins & d'Estampes*, Amsterdam, Vereenigde Drukkerijen, 1921. See also "Supplément," The Hague, Martinus Nijhoff, 1956.

A. M.

9

Foreword

WHEN in January and February 1956 there was an exhibition of Rubens' drawings and oil sketches at the Fogg Museum, many visitors noted that three objects in that exhibition, a drawing and two oil sketches, were lent by Mr. and Mrs. Curtis O. Baer. Each object had a special quality to commend it: power and boldness in the drawing, brilliance and fire in the *Elijah*, and subtlety and strength in the *St. Norbert*. Three works by Rubens in one private collection were an enviable number. It was an indication of more that might be revealed.

Mr. Baer is not a new collector nor is he a seeker after the spectacular. Except for the two oil sketches and a marble portrait *Head of Periander* that he lent to an exhibition of "Ancient Art in American Private Collections" in 1954–55, his collection is limited to drawings: not to drawings of any special school or country or epoch, but to any drawing which speaks to him in a way which prompts him to wish to continue to hear its voice. An active exporter, the first call on his energies and resources is the development of his own business. Since his affairs take him about the world, he has only limited time to look for drawings and less time than he would wish to study them and document their many relationships. Therefore, he greeted with enthusiasm our suggestion that he lend a selection to us for an exhibition, with the understanding that we would assemble the catalogue data relative to each.

Like the drawing collectors of the 17th and 18th centuries, Mr. Baer does not expose his drawings to the light. They are kept in solander boxes, from which they are taken for intimate enjoyment and close scrutiny. That fact in itself explains the character of the collection, the modest scale of the drawings and the freshness of vision. His sound university training in art history was not forgotten during the early business years. And, if the old masters were the ones best known at the beginning, an inquiring spirit, a sensitive eye and an open mind have prompted an understanding and appreciation of the modern masters, who are equally well represented.

The fact that the drawings are now shown in an exhibition does not indicate that the collector has reached a stopping point. In fact, this very month a notable addition has been made, Fra Bartolommeo's enchanting pen drawing *A View of Fiesole*. Regrettably it came just too late to be included in the catalogue. If the collector, during the weeks that his drawings are with us, is pausing, he is also reflecting and considering. Looking at what we have chosen, he finds that, even though the choice might not have been his own, it shows not only the scope of his interest but also his taste and his general aims.

The selection has been made by the compiler of the catalogue. If, for example, a Renoir and a Dutch drawing have been omitted that the owner might have included or a Cambiaso and a Marck added that he might not have selected, the scope of the collection is such that the general flavor of the whole has not been disturbed by the variations.

In this museum where we have so often and so proudly shown the drawing collections of our former students and colleagues, it gives us particular pleasure to welcome a collection with which we have only recently become familiar and whose contents were a delightful surprise. Rivalry in this limited field, which is contracting sharply as the supply diminishes, can only result in greater excitement and a by no means grudging admiration for those who find and acquire the fragile, yet paradoxically sturdy, objects of our enthusiasm. It is both instructive and inspiring to see what knowledge, enthusiasm, patience and an "eye" can quietly still accomplish.

AGNES MONGAN
Curator of Drawings

TITIAN (?) (1477 Pieve di Cadove–1576 Venice)

1. *Two Satyrs in a Landscape*

Two satyrs are seated in a landscape, one with his back turned holding the edge of an astrolabe, the other facing three-quarters front and leaning his right forearm on the hip of the first. A group of buildings crowns a hill in the right background.

Pen and bistre ink; 216 × 152 mm (8½ × 5¹⁵⁄₁₆ in.). Retouched in the faces, the leg and right arm of the satyr with his back turned and the forearm of the satyr looking out.
Watermark: Crossed arrows with a star above (similar to Briquet No. 6289).
Collections: Pembroke; Henry Oppenheimer.
Exhibitions: Five Centuries of Drawings, The Montreal Museum of Fine Arts, October–November 1953, No. 51, reproduced; *Symposium of the Graphic Arts,* Wesleyan University, Middletown, Connecticut, 1955.
References: The Henry Oppenheimer Collection, London, Christie, Manson & Woods, July 10–14, 1936, No. 42, p. 24; Tietze, H., and Tietze-Conrat, E., *Tizian-Studien, in Jahrbuch der Kunsthistorischen Sammlungen in Wien,* N. F., Vol. X, 1936, p. 169; Pallucchini, Rodolfo, *Sebastian Viniziano,* Milan, Casa Edetrice Mondadori, 1944, Plate 85; Tietze, H., and Tietze-Conrat, E., *The Drawings of the Venetian Painters of the 15th and 16th Centuries,* New York, 1944, No. 1948, Plate LIX (additional references are given in this volume); Tietze, H., *Titian,* London, 1950, Plate 7; Brendel, Otto, "Borrowings from Ancient Art in Titian," *The Art Bulletin,* 1955, p. 118.

Comment: When K. T. Parker compiled the catalogue of the Oppenheimer Collection, he listed this drawing under the name of Domenico Campagnola. He noted, however, that he had little conviction about the attribution. On the contrary he felt that there was an affinity of feeling with the works of Dosso Dossi. That same year, 1936, the Tietzes published the drawing as Titian. In 1944 Dr. Pallucchini published it as Sebastiano del Piombo. Then it appeared again as Titian: in the *Drawings of the Venetian Painters,* 1948, and in H. Tietze's monograph of 1950. It was shown in Montreal in 1953 with an attribution to Titian. Dr. Brendel cited it in his article of 1955 on Titian's borrowings, but in the summer of 1957 he observed certain similarities of style which recall Dosso Dossi. Professor Freedberg (orally) also considered that it is by Titian. With so much weight given to that attribution and since the drawing is most widely known under Titian's name, we have so listed it.

Questions of attribution aside, the astrological content of the drawing and the interpretations that can be drawn from it make it fascinating and unique. On this problem we consulted Eric Schroeder, who has a fund of astrological knowledge.

He finds that there is not a single detail in the drawing which does not allow an astrological interpretation. His elaboration of this statement is so extensive that it cannot be quoted here (we hope that it can be published elsewhere). Perhaps the most crucial comment that he makes is that he finds strong internal evidence that the horoscope was drawn between January 20/21 and April 8/9, 1513. Since Mr. Schroeder believes the drawing to be by Titian, the great part of his interpretation is in reference to Titian's life. Dr. Brendel,[1] who has also considered the astrological content, agrees with Mr. Schroeder that the sphere does not represent a complete horoscope, but differs with him in the rest of his interpretation, even in the time of year emphasized. He points out that in the horoscope or astrolabe the sun possesses major importance. Because of that fact and because Alfonso d'Este, Duke of Ferrera, prided himself on being a child of Leo (he was born July 21), Dr. Brendel wonders if the drawing has some connection with the decoration of Alfonso's famous "studio."[2] Ruth W. Kennedy suggested that there might be a connection with the Farnesina.

The problem of attribution is made more difficult because the drawing has suffered, something it is difficult to see in the reproduction. Part of the seeming coarseness of the faces and the contours is due to the retouching of a clumsy later hand. Yet, taking condition as well as style into consideration, and after an exploration of the Dossi suggestion, we feel that Dr. Pallucchini is closer to a solution when he assigns the drawing to Sebastiano del Piombo. Mrs. Kennedy's suggestion of a Farnesina connection is provocative.

Sebastiano del Piombo was called to Rome by Agostino Chigi in 1511. He played a very important part in the decoration of the Sala di Galatea of the Farnesina. Dr. Saxl has pointed out that the whole scheme of decoration of the Sala di Galatea is a veiled horoscope. It is one which he carefully deciphered.[3] Sebastiano painted the lunettes in 1511 and the Polyphemus, which is next to Raphael's *Galatea*, in 1513.[4] The drawing for the *Polyphemus* in the Musée Wicar at Lille[5] is strikingly like the Baer drawing in handling. The artists who worked giving pictorial expression to Chigi's astrological plan must have been initiated into the mysteries and meanings of astrology. The horoscope of the ceiling of the Sala di Galatea is cast according to Dr. Beer[6] for someone born the first of December, 1466. Chigi's actual birthday is not known, but there is no doubt that the ceiling is his horoscope. Although Mr. Schroeder interprets the horoscope according to Titian's life, he notes, ". . . taking

Mars' position as in the end of Pisces or the beginning of Aries, our concern narrows within the period appropriate to the drawing's style to years 1466, 1481, 1498, 1508, 1513, 1545, in all of which Mars was on that date in such a position."[7] It is striking that 1466 is the first date he notices and that 1513 also occurs as the probable date the horoscope was drawn.

At the time of his arrival in Rome, Sebastiano was an artist steeped in the Venetian style of the early 16th century. Several drawings which used to be attributed to Domenico Campagnola have in recent years been given to Sebastiano.[8] (Dr. Brendel notes that a Campagnola engraving[9] has an astrological sphere not unlike this one.) In Rome Sebastiano was plunged into the milieu which was transforming the arts. Michelangelo was working on the Sistine Ceiling and Raphael on the frescoes of the Stanza della Segnatura.

Making no reference to the astrological content, Dr. Pallucchini dates the Baer drawing 1510.[10] Since it is not connected with any fresco, it is possible that it may have been drawn a little later. It was several years before Michelangelo's overwhelming influence obliterated all vestiges of Sebastiano's Venetian training. It may be that further exploration will confirm both the proposed date of 1513 and a connection with Chigi's astrological schemes.

1. Letter to Agnes Mongan, August 21, 1957.

2. Eugenio Battista, "Disegni Inediti di Tiziano e Lo Studio D'Alfonso D'Este," *Commentari*, No. 3, 1954, pp. 191–216.

3. Fritz Saxl, *La Fede Astrologica di Agostino Chigi* (Rome: Reale Accademia d'Italia, 1934).

4. Luitpold Dussler, *Sebastiano del Piombo* (Basel: Holbein-Verlag, 1942), p. 139.

5. *Ibid.*, Plate 91.

6. Saxl, p. 28.

7. Memorandum to Agnes Mongan, summer 1957.

8. Rodolfo Pallucchini, *Sebastian Viniziano* (Milan: Casa Editrice Mondadori, 1944).

9. A. M. Hind, *Early Italian Engraving* (London: Bernard Quaritch, Ltd., 1948), Part II, Vol. VII, Plate 777.

10. Pallucchini, p. 37.

FLORENTINE, ca. 1460

2. *Standing Draped Figure Seen from the Back*

A youthful figure with a heavy drapery over his left shoulder and under his right arm, steps forward on his right foot, as he looks up to the left.

Pen and bistre wash on white paper; 113×35 mm (4½ × 1⅜ in.).

Comment: The drawing, which has not previously been published, has been attributed to that always-nebulous personage, Maso Finiguerra. In the sensitive drawing of the face with its gentle and delicate expression and in the firm, springing step of the left foot, there is more surety and artistry than there is in the awkward and somewhat shaky contours of the apprentices in the drawings often attributed to Finiguerra. The suggestion of movement, the treatment of the drapery with its deep folds, and the drawing of the hair all bespeak an artist who had felt and absorbed Fra Angelico's influence. Although tiny in scale, the figure has a noble and serene air. So far it has not been found in any Florentine painting. It seems to us closer, however, to the figure of Nathan in Pesellino's *The Penitence of King David* and to some of the figures which surround the chariot of *Love* in the Fenway Court Cassone given to the same artist, than it is to Pollaiuolo to whom the so-called "Finiguerra Figures" have often been attributed.

BARTOLOMMEO PASSEROTTI
(1520 Bologna–1592 Bologna)

3. *Sketches*

Recto: A left arm, seen from the back, is outstretched towards the left; above it in the left center is a seated woman leaning over something in her lap; at right center is an arm; further to the right is a profile, turned left, and a standing Madonna holding a child; at the upper left corner on the half-turned page is a seated female nude and a half-length figure of a bearded man in left profile.

Verso: At the upper left is a seated nude youth seen from the back;

at the center, a male figure striding left, body turned right; and at the lower right are sketches of a vertebra.

Pen and acid ink on white paper; 290 × 200 mm (11 7/16 × 7 7/8 in.).
Watermark: Angel in a circle (?)
Collections: Dr. L. Pollak's stamp on verso at lower left (L. 788b).

Comment: A hand as quick, nervous and mannered as the drawing has made written notations on both the front and back of the drawing which are only partially decipherable. On the recto above the shoulder at the right is written, "Io che paegr (?) / di tal vasta no / saglio (?)." Below the arm is repeated, "Io che pagrav (?)." On the verso to the right of the vertebra is written, "questa / parte / un / posta / adosso / ," followed by three undecipherable lines. At the left are more undecipherable words. The figure on the back seems to have been copied either from the Belvedere *Torso* or from a copy of it.

The outstretched arm has the strongly accented contours and the closely woven crosshatching which distinguish the vocabulary of those mannerist artists who followed and imitated Michelangelo. The feeling for the bony structure so close beneath the skin is typical of other drawings attributed to Passerotti. The woman bending over might be plucking a fowl. Her posture suggests that the drawing may have been done at the time that Passerotti painted the *Poultry Market Women* in the Collection of Professor Longhi.[1]

1. See Heinrich Bodmer, "Die Kunst des Bartolomeo Passarotti," *Belvedere*, 1938–39, Heft ¼, Plate 88.

CIRCLE OF FEDERIGO ZUCCARO
(1542? San Angelo in Vado–1609 Ancona)

4. *Moses, Aaron and Hur at the Battle of Israel and Amalek*

In the left upper corner Aaron and Hur support the arms of kneeling Moses, who lifts his hands in prayer toward a vision of God in a cloud. Below them, filling the right and lower corners of the drawing and separated by a diagonal of banners and horses, rages the battle of Israel and Amalek, men and horses intertwined. At the right upper portion of the drawing tents of a camp are visible.

Brown ink and washes with pen and brush over black chalk; 274 × 405 mm (10¹³⁄₁₆ × 16 in.).
Exhibitions: Pontormo to Greco; The Age of Mannerism, John Heron Art Museum, Indianapolis, 1954, No. 36.

Comment: Federigo Zuccaro and his many assistants painted in Rome, Caprarola, Florence and Venice as well as in France, Spain, Flanders, Holland and England. A great many drawings survive, some of which are directly related to the storytelling frescoes which were so admired in the 16th century. The drawings are mannerist designs in their movement, their flourishes of line for its own sake, their evident love of contrapposto, and their use of a rather airless space.

This scene illustrates EXODUS 17:8–16, which describes how the Israelites were successful in battle with Amalek only as long as Moses' arms were held up to the Lord. Between 1561 and 1563 Zuccaro painted two fresco series devoted to the story of Moses. One, which showed 16 scenes, was in the great gallery of the Belvedere at the Vatican, a series in which Baroccio was his assistant. The other three scenes are in a ceiling of the Casino of Pius IV.

GIOVANNI FRANCESCO BARBIERI
called GUERCINO
(1591 Cento–1666 Bologna)

5. *Esther and Ahasuerus*

A crowned woman seen in three-quarter view on the left approaches a bearded and turbaned man. He recoils from her, resting on his left arm; his right hand is raised to his chest. In the left hand he holds a thin staff. Although his face is seen in profile, his body is turned almost parallel to the picture plane. Both figures are half-length.

Pen and brown ink; 180 × 235 mm (7³⁄₁₆ × 9¼ in.).
Collections: Jan Pietersz, Zoomer (L. 1511); Mrs. Ralph Booth, Detroit.

Comment: Denis Mahon suggests that this is "possibly an early study connected with the Esther and Ahasuerus composition of 1639 which was formerly in the Barberini Collection. In the final version, however,

Esther is shown in a faint, supported by two attendants."[1] An engraving after Guercino's painting done by Robert Strange[2] in 1767 shows the main figures reversed.

1. Letter to Agnes Mongan, 13 July 1957.
2. Charles LeBlanc, *Catalogue de l'Œuvre de Robert Strange, Graveur* (Leipzig, 1848), No. 2.

6. *Landscape with Bridge and Figures*

Near the foreground a woman, holding a child, and a man stand on a promontory of land. A dog swims towards them from a river which winds under a double-arched bridge into the middle ground. Trees and bushes flank the bridge: a figure leans upon it watching the foreground scene. Further in the distance there is a bluff on the right and a level plain with trees and buildings to the left and in the center.

Pen and brown ink; 160 × 194 mm (6⅝ × 7¾ in.).
Collections: Freiherr Richard von Kuehlmann.

Comment: The quick, sure, parallel straight strokes which indicate the foreground, the bridge and the road are as characteristic of Guercino's landscape drawings as the extremely agitated calligraphic lines of the preceding drawing are of his figure drawings. Great quantities of both survive, as do numberless imitations, especially imitations of the 18th century. These two drawings seem, however, to be by Guercino himself, although neither can be definitively linked with a known painting.

LUCA CAMBIASO (1527 Mongelia–1585 Madrid)

7. *Christ on the Way to Emmaus*

Christ, distinguished by the rays of light that shine around his head, strides purposefully forward toward the left, in animated conversation with the Apostle at the right, while the Apostle at the left listens with acute attention. All three figures are dressed in 16th-century costume: halos hang above the head of the two Apostles. Christ and the Apostle at the left wear pilgrims' hats, and Christ carries over his shoulder a beribboned staff (the labarum?).

Pen and acid ink on white paper; 308 × 234 mm (12⅛ × 9⅛ in.).
Watermark: A siren holding her bifurcated tail in each hand, an indication of the sea below (somewhat similar to Briquet 13876–78, all of which were of Genoese origin).

Comment: This and the following drawing present two different views of the same scene, as though the artist had made a quick sketch of the group as the lively figures approached him and then another after they had passed him (although in the first it is the Apostle at Christ's right who wears a hat and in the second, it is the Apostle on the left).

Both are drawn in Cambiaso's characteristic pen style of quick, dashing lines with little hook-like ends, lines which create figures of energy and movement but no weight. Cambiaso often drew a whole series of drawings on a single theme: for example, the *Rest on the Flight into Egypt*, the *Adoration of the Magi*, the *Descent from the Cross*. Another drawing showing the group moving from left to right, but drawn in more summary fashion, the heads little more than cubes and the figures more severely simplified, was in the Benno Geiger Collection.[1]

1. Leo Planiscig and Hermann Voss, *Handzeichnungen alter Meister aus D. Sammlung Geiger* (Zurich: Amalthea Verlag), Plate 54.

8. *Christ on the Way to Emmaus* (Going)

The group is walking away from the spectator along a road that leads into the distance. In the left background is a town on the crown of a hill.

Pen and acid ink on white paper; 335 × 248 mm (13¼ × 9¾ in.).

Comment: Another version of this drawing exists in the Besançon Museum (Inv. D1458). The Besançon version, however, is shaded with wash and there is no suggestion of landscape above the figures. Although Cambiaso is known to have drawn many versions of the same scene, the hesitant duplication of lines in the Besançon drawing suggests that it is a copy made after this one, probably by one of Cambiaso's students.

GIOVANNI BATTISTA TIEPOLO
(1696 Venice–1770 Madrid)

9. *Figure of a Man*

A clean-shaven, young man wearing a turban is seen in steep fore-shortening from below. He looks downward toward the left, his arms stretched out toward the right.

Pen and bistre wash; 238 × 199 mm (9⅜ × 7⅞ in.).
Watermark: a five-petalled flower with stem and a single leaf (similar to Briquet No. 6446).
The page is numbered 127 in pencil at the lower right.

Comment: Although there are hundreds of figures steeply foreshortened (standing on clouds, stepping on copings, borne aloft into the heavens), we have found no figure which corresponds to this one. The staccato lines of the hands and the character of the contours lead us to place it in the period of the Würzburg frescoes (1750–53), that is, at the very height of Tiepolo's powers. Among the thousands of drawings which survive, there are many, like this, of single figures sharply projected into brilliant sunlight, a few essential lines and a few touches of transparent wash bringing each into existence on the white page. Morassi,[1] in his chapter on the drawings and prints of Tiepolo, has noted the difficulties of trying to date the enormous number of surviving drawings, calling attention at the same time to the few which can with certainty be assigned to certain periods. Among the drawings which he reproduces is one preserved in Trieste[2] actually dated "17 Febr. 1744" which in the speed and accents of its line and brevity and surety of its wash has strong similarities to this drawing. Five other drawings at Trieste can also be compared to it.[3]

1. Antonio Morassi, *Tiepolo* (Bergamo: Istituto Italiano d'Arti Grafiche, 1943).
2. *Ibid.*, Plate 137.
3. Giorgio Vigni, *Disegni del Tiepolo* (Padova: Le Tre Venezie, 1942), Plates 72, 164, 165, 199 and 200.

SALVATOR ROSA (1615 Naples–1673 Rome)

10. *Two Men Discover the Body of a Third Man*

A man lies prostrate on the ground at the left, his body sharply foreshortened with his bent legs toward the viewer, his arms outstretched, his head thrown back inward. In the center a second figure moves forward and bends over to look at the prostrate figure and raises his hands in horror. A third figure, of youthful aspect, wearing a short, wind-blown tunic, turns to look down over his right shoulder as he walks towards the right and points with his upraised left arm to the upper right corner, as if to summon help.

Pen and bistre wash on white paper; 197 × 189 mm (7¾ × 7⁷⁄₁₆ in.).
Collections: Sir Thomas Lawrence (L. 2445); Miss MacIntosh.

Comment: A painter of religious pictures, landscapes and, above all, of battle scenes, a poet and a musician whose talent and turbulent personality won him many admirers and patrons, Rosa is remembered even today perhaps as much for the drama of his own life as for any profound knowledge of his work. Careless as he often was in his painting and hasty as his drawings show him to have been, he yet did trouble to work out in drawings the poses and gestures of the figures in many of his paintings. Occasionally he drew in chalk or crayon; more often the pen seemed more suited to the speed and stenographic character of his nervous line. This drawing does not have the nervous abruptness of the drawings reproduced by Schmidt[1] from the collection of about 200 in the Leipzig Stadtbibliothek, or the drawing in the Metropolitan Museum of Art.[2]

The manner of indicating in single short lines nose, mouth and chin, and his shorthand for upraised fingers as well as the angular folds of drapery, place it closer to a drawing, *A Group of Men and Women*, in the Louvre,[3] a drawing twice inscribed with Rosa's name in an early hand. Although the group in this drawing has not been identified in any painting or etching of Rosa's, the figure at the right is, in type and movement, almost precisely, if reversed, that of the angel in *Angel Leaving Tobias* at Chantilly, a painting which the French took in 1802 from the Sta. Maria del Popolo, for which Rosa had painted it. Rosa left a large volume of his drawings to his heirs. He also, we know from his correspondence, presented drawings to his acquaintances. Schmidt quotes a letter to Ricciardi in which Rosa speaks of his drawings and the fact that he needs them by him while he works. The date of the letter, 1652, would indicate that he used them when he was painting the masterpieces of his Roman period. None of that group was signed. Perhaps this drawing was once part of that group.

1. A. W. Schmidt, "Drawings by Salvator Rosa in the Leipzig Stadtbibliothek," *Old Master Drawings*, Vol. VI (March 1932), pp. 60–61, Plates 53–56.
2. *European Drawings from the Collections of the Metropolitan Museum of Art*, I, "Italian Drawings," No. 30.
3. Archives, No. 3832.

GIOVANNI BATTISTA PIAZZETTA
(1682 Pietrarossa–1754 Venice)

11. *A Young Man Embracing a Girl*

At the right a young man in a close-fitting cap seen in profile towards the left, circles with his right arm the shoulders of a young girl, who looks down towards the left and places her right hand on his left shoulder.

Black charcoal heightened with white on blue paper, faded to grey-brown; 396 × 315 mm (15⅝ × 12½ in.).
Watermark: HP or HR
Collections: H. A. Vivian Smith.

Comment: Pallucchini,[1] who has devoted years of study to the work of Piazzetta, records in his most recent monograph the fact that the great Venetian artist drew constantly. Many of his finest drawings have come to light only in recent years. As Pallucchini notes, they fall into two distinct categories: in the first are the drawings in charcoal heightened with white, which show, for the most part, only heads drawn nearly life-size. In the second category are the chalk drawings for groups of figures or whole-composition drawings which were transposed by engravers into text illustrations in 18th-century books. The drawings of the first category Piazzetta sold as surrogates, in Pallucchini's phrase, for the paintings which would have taken more time. They had an immediate success not only in Venice but also abroad.

Such heads seem to have almost the breath of life in them. A vibrant light gently defines their distinguishing, individual features. The artist suggests the very bloom of a youthful skin and records the subtlest fleeting expressions. Zanetti[2] wrote as early as 1733 that "more beautiful drawings of this kind have never been seen." The famous English collector, Consul Joseph Smith, who was responsible for sending so much of the work of Guardi and Canaletto to England, had a large collection of

Piazzetta drawings, many of which are now in Windsor Castle. This particular one, although it was engraved by Giovanni Cattini in his series, "Icones ad Virum Expressae," in 1763[3] has, as far as we know, not been reproduced since the 18th century.

As in the others of its kind, the light comes from the upper left, casting the shadows to the right. White touches mark the light on the foreheads just below the hair line, along the profile of the nose, beneath the eyes, on the edge of the chin and along the rim of the ear. The paper, pieced as frequently happens along the right edge, is now browned by time as in many other Piazzetta drawings, but it was probably grey-blue.

The models appear in other drawings. Piazzetta frequently drew heads in pairs. It is often impossible to date his drawings, since the artist often repeated years later, with variations, a figure which he had done before. The boy and girl of this drawing appear in several others. The girl seems a little older than she appears in a drawing in the Venice Academy,[4] but about the same age as the study for Rebecca[5] which Pallucchini dates 1738–40. The young man seems, however, to be about the same age as the youth in a drawing at Windsor Castle.[6] Each is to be found in a different Windsor drawing. The whole Windsor series Pallucchini places at a rather later date than the Venice series because of a greater softness of form and a more pleasing expressiveness.

This particular page happily retains a sparkle and freshness which few others have kept.

1. Rodolfo Pallucchini, *Piazzetta* (Milan: Aldo Martello Editore, 1956).
2. *Ibid.*, p. 47.
3. G. K. Nagler, *Künstler-Lexicon* (Munich: Verlag von E. A. Fleischmann, 1835), Vol. II, pp. 440–441.
4. Pallucchini, Plate 161.
5. *Ibid.*, Plate 144.
6. *Ibid.*, Plate 164.

BARTOLOMÉ ESTEBAN MURILLO
(1617 Seville–1682 Seville)

12. *St. Joseph and the Young Christ*

St. Joseph, seated on a rock, supports the young Christ, who is standing on his knee. Jesus has his right arm around the neck of the full-bearded rather young Joseph.

Pen, brush and bistre wash on white paper. 250 × 192 mm (9⁷⁄₁₆ × 7³⁄₁₆ in.).
Watermark: MCGG
The remains of a former mat of coarser laid paper are still attached to the drawing.
At the top, on the added portion, written in a 17th-century hand is "bartolome mu-
rillo f." Undecipherable writing, top and bottom, is also on the added paper. The pa-
per of the original drawing has been folded horizontally.

Comment: The appearance in art of St. Joseph in any position but a sub-
ordinate and auxiliary one occurs for the first time in the 16th century.
During the Counter Reformation St. Joseph was favored by the numerous new religious orders as the personification of poverty, chastity and
obedience. With this rise in popularity, which was especially great in
Spain, came also the problem of visual depiction. In the Middle Ages
Joseph was always represented as an old man. In this drawing, and in
most of the other paintings and drawings that Murillo did of the subject,
he followed the new trend and depicted Joseph as a dark-bearded mature
man—the loving protector of the Holy Child and thus the important
symbol of the father of a unified family.

Although Murillo did several paintings of the theme, none corresponds directly to this drawing of the full length Joseph and Christ who is
no longer an infant. The drawing is both warm and tender, without the
super-sentimentality and sweetness of many of Murillo's paintings. The
composition is well knit. A warm brown wash gives a softness to the
over-all drawing, correlating nicely with the staccato lines.

Drawings related in style to this one can be found in the Louvre, Archives numbers 2477, 3014, and 2508. The latter is also connected in subject matter, as is number 3121.

MASTER OF THE TOBIT LEGEND (?)

13. *Jacob's Dream*

Jacob, his cloak drawn around him, his staff beneath his right
hand, lies asleep in the foreground. Behind him angels are mounting
and descending a ladder set against a cloud. At the top of the ladder,
leaning over the top rung, is the Lord. In the left middle distance
Jacob is departing with Leah from Laban's house. In the right mid-

dle distance Jacob is embracing Rachel as she brings the sheep and cattle to be watered at the well.

Pen and ink on brown paper; 210 × 184 mm (8 ⅜ × 7¼ in.) (The drawing was measured through the center because it is an oval flattened at the sides.).

Comment: The drawing is one of a series related to each other and to glass rondels. The author has been given the name Master of the Tobit Legend since the best known drawings of the series tell the story of Tobit. There are others, however, which tell the stories of Jacob and Joseph.[1] The complicated relationship of drawings to painted rondels has not yet been worked out. Dr. Boon of the Amsterdam Print Room[2] has called our attention to some of the problems: the borrowings from paintings by Brussels and Ghent masters, the relationship to figures in miniatures by the pseudo-Alexander Benning, the presence of different styles and techniques not only in the painted rondels but also in the drawings which may have served as preparatory drawings or as copies from the rondels for other artists. Mr. Popham, who first gave the Tobit Master his name, describes the use of the painted rondels as decoration for the windows of living rooms and domestic chapels in 15th-century Flanders.[3] He notes that the earliest type which survives in any quantity in drawings and in glass is connected with the School of Hugo van der Goes. In the Baer drawing the figures in the right background of Jacob and Rachel derive from the central figures of Jacob and Rachel in Van der Goes' famous drawing at Christ Church, Oxford. The gestures and movement of the figures are the same, although the costumes are different. The artist of the Baer drawing does not seem to us to be identical with the author of the Tobit drawing preserved at Windsor Castle.[4] His characteristics are rather those carefully scrutinized and described by Friedländer as the traits of another anonymous master whom he has named the Joseph Master,[5] a master who seems to have spent most of his life in Brussels and to be a follower of Roger van der Weyden. In the Baer drawing there is the same outlining of nose and eyes, and small pockets of shadow at the corners of the mouth. There is also the careless drawing of the figures in the background which Edward King speaks of in his enumeration of the Joseph Master's characteristics.[6] The costume of Jacob closely resembles that worn by the figure in the left of the rondel of *Joseph Recounting His Dream*,[7] and the manner in which the artist has fitted his foreground and background figures and sheep into the oval has strong parallels in the rondel of *Joseph Cast in the Well* of the Kaiser Friedrich

Museum.[8] Further studies by the specialists will, we hope, throw more light on the problem of the attribution of this drawing, which was done in Flanders about 1500.

1. K. T. Parker, *Catalogue of the Collection of Drawings in the Ashmolean Museum* (Oxford: The Clarendon Press, 1938), Vol. I, p. 4, No. 8.
2. Letter to Agnes Mongan, July 13, 1957.
3. A. E. Popham, "Notes on Flemish Domestic Glass Painting—I," *Apollo, A Journal of the Arts*, Vol. VII, Jan.–June, 1928, p. 175.
4. *Ibid.*, Fig. 1.
5. Max J. Friedländer, *Die Altniederländische Malerei* (Berlin: Paul Cassirer, 1926), Vol. IV, No. 79, Plates LXII and LXIII.
6. Edward S. King, "Two Panels by the Master of the Joseph Legend," *The Journal of the Walters Art Gallery*, 1943, p. 41–47.
7. Friedländer, Plate LXI.
8. King, p. 42, Fig. 2.

SWISS MASTER (?), First Quarter of the 16th Century

14. *Group of Nude Figures*

They stand in a kind of loose circle: five nude men wearing Roman helmets and carrying ornate tridents, and three nude women, each with a piece of transparent drapery held loosely around her hips.

Brush drawing heightened with white on paper prepared with a green ground; 287×214 mm (11 5/16 × 8 7/16 in.).
Inscribed at the right above the heads: 1522.
Collections: Prince Liechtenstein.
References: Schönbrunner and Meder, *Handzeichnungen alter Meister aus der Albertina und anderen Sammlungen*, Band XII, No. 1432.

Comment: This drawing remains a mystery in both its subject matter and its place of origin. Although it was formerly placed with the Flemish drawings, we prefer to place it in Switzerland, perhaps in the following of Hans Leu. It has not the strength nor drama of Leu's own hand, but the figures are related to his. The artist who made the drawing was clearly left-handed for all the shading along the contours is in parallel, short, fine lines that go from upper left to lower right. Dr. Panofsky, who finds the drawing German rather than Swiss in character, suggests that since the standards which the men hold seem to have been inspired by those illustrated in Francesco Colonna's *Hypnerotomachia Poliphili*,[1] possibly this drawing is a fragment of a design for a triumph.[2]

1. Francesco Colonna, *Hypnerotomachia Poliphili*, *VBI Humana Omnia non nisi Somnium esse Ostendit, at que Obiter Plurima Scitu Sanequam Digna Comemorat* (London: Methuen & Co., 1904), x.

2. Letter to Agnes Mongan, November 19, 1957.

MAARTEN VAN HEEMSKERCK
(1498 Heemskerk–1574 Haarlem)

15. *Triumph of Job*

Job, naked except for a piece of roughly woven cloth laid over his lap, is seated on the back of a huge tortoise. In his left hand he holds the staff of a tattered banner which is decorated with a heart supported by wings above the scales of Justice, a flaming sword and the orb of the world. In his right hand he has gathered the robes which are tied around the waists of those who follow him: the devil, his wife and his friends, Eliphaz, Bildad and Zophar. In the right background Job sits naked mourning on the earth. His three friends mourn with him while Job's wife harangues the group. Job's cattle lie dead near him and his house is consumed by flames behind him.

Pen and brown ink; 182×262 mm (7⅛ × 10⅜ in.).
Signed and dated at the lower right: "M. vã Haemskerch/1559 inventor."
The contours have been lightly incised.
Collections: Freiherr Richard von Kuehlmann.
Exhibitions: Symposium of the Graphic Arts, Middletown, Connecticut, Wesleyan University, 1955.

Comment: The drawing is one of a series of eight designed by Van Heemskerck and published by Jan Galle. The series bears the title "Patientiae Triumphus." The first of the series represents Patience herself. The others are triumphs of Isaac, Joseph, David, Tobit, St. Stephen and Christ. Job is the fifth in the group.[1] Hollstein records that the drawings for the Isaac, Joseph and Stephen were in the Koenigs Collection. The influence of Heemskerck's years in Rome are clearly reflected not only in the architectural background but in the mannerist style in which he has drawn the elongated figures. Many Heemskerck drawings for prints survive; perhaps the largest single group is in the Copenhagen Print Room.

1. F. W. H. Hollstein, *Dutch and Flemish Etchings Engravings and Woodcuts* (Amsterdam: Menno Hertzberger), Vol. III, p. 240, No. 120–127.

MAARTEN VAN HEEMSKERCK (?)

16. *Roman Landscape*

Several well-known ruins have been brought together to make the composition. A fragment of the entablature of the Temple of Concord dominates the scene in the center. In front of it is the Campanile of S. Francesca Romana half concealed by Roman ruins. At the right is a bit of the Colosseum; across the foreground, further ruins in Roman brick. Beyond the leafless tree in the left middle distance is a view of fields with three towers marking off a crenelated wall.

Pen and ink on white paper; 207×291 mm (8⅛ × 11½ in.).
Collections: Nathaniel Hone (L. 2793 stamp at lower right).

Comment: The drawing has borne an attribution to Heemskerck. A careful comparison of it with many of the views reproduced by Egger in his *Römische Veduten*[1] leads one to wonder if it is not perhaps nearer to the master that Egger calls the Anonymous Fabriczy, although the airiness and sense of sunlight is somewhat more perceptible and marked here than in the drawings of that anonymous master. In any event, the drawing was made by a northern artist who visited Rome in the second half of the 16th century.

1. Hermann Egger, *Römische Veduten* . . . (Wien & Leipzig: F. Wolfrum & Co., 1911–31).

PIETER BRUEGHEL, THE ELDER
(1525? Dutch-Belgian Border–1569 Brussels)

17. *Recto: Studies of Peasants*

At the left a peasant, with fur-trimmed hat set deeply over his head revealing only the nose and the prominent jaw, a full-sleeved and skirted short jacket caught in at the waist, loose breeches tucked into his boots, is seated on a bench in left profile with his hardly visible hands clasped on his knees. The right knee and left foot are cut by the edges of the paper.

At the right a peasant woman with cap and attached scarf wrapping up all of her head but the profiled nose, mouth and triangular piece of cheek, carries on her back a huge basket, covered by a mantle which falls from her shoulders in folds below her waist. She stands in left profile with her left arm raised as if to grasp a walking stick. Her feet are not visible.

Pen in light brown ink over black chalk; 100×140 mm (3¹⁵⁄₁₆ × 5½ in.).
Inscribed at lower left: "nar leven." Indications of the color of the costumes are given: behind the woman's hat, "swarthe mus" (black cap); behind her collar, "wit" (white); behind her cape, "swarthe mantel" (black cape); near her skirt, "swarthe rock" (black skirt); behind the man's hat, "grisse mus" (grey cap); behind his jacket, "omberre rock" (yellow-brown tunic); behind his stockings, "witte kousen" (white stockings).

18. *Verso: Studies of Peasants*

A peasant with a prominent profile stands at the left dressed in a baggy shirt and breeches. His hands and feet are not indicated. At the right is a view from the back of the peasant woman of Recto.

Black chalk. The dark lines of the woman's hat and the man's breeches seem to be the work of a restorer.
Watermark: The letter "W" beneath a fragment of a design.
Collections: Prince Liechtenstein.
Exhibitions: Five Centuries of Drawings, The Montreal Museum of Fine Arts, October–November 1953, No. 7, reproduced.
References: Kurz, Otto, "Drei Zeichnungen Pieter Brueghels des Älteren," *Die Graphischen Künste*, Neue Folge, Band I, 1936, p. 5, Fig. 2; Tolnay, Charles de, *The Drawings of Pieter Brueghel, the Elder*, Salzburg, R. Kiesel. Recto: No. 82, Plate LIV-top; Verso: Addenda 2, not reproduced.

Comment: Between 1557 and 1569, Brueghel did numerous drawings inscribed "nar het leven" (from life). Tolnay places this drawing among them in the period 1559–63. Kurz dismisses the earlier view that "nar leven" means a sketchbook from real life: the peasants are idealized through a kind of abstraction, and no emphasis is placed on facial characteristics. The majority are viewed from the back or side and are represented in terms of posture and clothing: her basket makes the woman in the drawing into a hunchback. Are these then not sketches but rather finished works? Kurz, arguing that they are somewhere in between, mainly intends to question Tolnay's rather philosophical thesis that "they are neither preparatory studies nor direct copies from nature, but they are methodical studies of the essence of nature as it is manifested in man as a product of nature." Tolnay, however, is certainly right to point out the difference between the still detachment of these peasant drawings and the vivacious movement of the painted figures in *Les Cycles des Paysans*, for which Kurz and others assume they may have been the sketched studies.

JAN GOSSAERT, called MABUSE
(ca. 1478 Mauberge–1533 Antwerp)

19. *Old Testament Scene* (?)

A turbaned and bearded elder, a scepter in his right hand, a sword at his left side, a veil floating from the peak of his conical hat, strides forward, his left arm held high. In front of him is a classical pilaster with Roman armor in bas-relief surmounted by Gothic leaves. In a Gothic niche above it sits a bearded man wearing a crown. In the left background a man in a broad-brimmed hat, wearing Roman armor and also carrying a scepter, starts down a steep flight of steps. Under the porch, almost concealed by columns, a woman seems to follow him. Turrets, tracery, friezes, medallions and vines fill the page.

Pen and ink; 185 × 90 mm (7⅜ × 3½ in.).
Watermark: fragmentary (the figure "4" suspended from a circle?)
Dated on the plinth of the pilaster: 1521.
Collections: Valori; E. Rodrigues.
References: Frederik Muller & Cie, Amsterdam, 12–13 Juillet 1921, No. 31, Plate x.

Comment: Dr. Wescher has pointed out that the numerous drawings by Gossaert are very varied and give "a lively record of his intellectual experiences and the constant interchange between his Gothic and Renaissance conceptions."[1] Until recent years only very few of his drawings were known, but in the past two or three decades scholars have published a variety of drawings that are clearly from his hand, so that now about 35 of his drawings are known. A stylistic examination of them permits the establishment of a chronology. His early manner can be approximately dated from the years just preceding, during, and following his journey to Rome with his patron, Philip the Good of Burgundy (1508–09). There follows a group which corresponds to his painting style in the years 1511–15. Finally, there is a later group, larger in scale, freer in handling and more varied in technique, from the years 1515 until his death in 1533.

The Baer drawing, small in scale and of small pen lines, closely parallel, with a strong flavor of the Antwerp mannerists in its love of elaboration for its own sake, is clearly in Gossaert's early manner. Therefore, we would guess that the date 1521, although in a 16th-century hand, was added sometime after the drawing was made. The mixture of Italian details (the pilasters, the profile in a medallion, the grouped, round columns) with the trefoils and crockets of late Gothic ornament speak for a time shortly after the Italian journey. It would seem, however, a little earlier than the drawings it most closely resembles in spirit, style and theme, the *Augustus and the Tiburtine Sibyl* in the Berlin Print Room[2] and the *Adoration of the Kings* in the Louvre.

1. Paul Wescher, "An Unnoticed Drawing by Jan Gossaert in the Morgan Library," *The Art Quarterly*, XII (Summer 1949), 262.
2. F. Winkler, "Jan Gossaert, called Mabuse," *Old Master Drawings*, No. 38, September, 1935, p. 30, Plate 31.

ABRAHAM BLOEMAERT (1564 Dordrecht–1651 Utrecht)

20. *Adam and Eve*

Eve faces front, her right arm held up to the left, her weight on her right foot. Adam, in profile towards the left, steps forward, his right foot in front of Eve's right, his head turned inward to look at her. Her left fingers are intertwined with his right ones. In his left hand he holds a branch with apple leaves.

Sanguine on pale tan paper; 295 × 194 mm (11⅝ × 7⅝ in.).
Watermark: A crown surmounted by a cross above a monogram of two capital C's intertwined back to back, a trefoil and the letter B suspended from the monogram.

Comment: In Bloemaert's exceedingly long, busy and productive life his style underwent many changes, although always his drawings are distinguished by mannerist traits: a love of intertwining forms and movement, elongated shapes and a strong sense of the decorative value of a design on a page. There is an elegance about these two figures that has almost a French flavor. Bloemaert never went to Italy, but he did spend five years (1580–85) in Paris. Some influence from that visit may show in this drawing. It is also clear that he must have known Goltzius' engraving after Spranger's *Adam and Eve*.[1]

1. See Otto Hirschmann, *Hendrick Goltzius* (Leipzig: Von Klinkhardt & Biermann), Tafel IX.

HENDRICK GOLTZIUS   (1558 Mulbrecht–1616 Haarlem)

21. *Head of a Young Gentleman*

He is seated facing three-quarters front, leaning forward, his right elbow on a table, his right hand held against the side of his head. He wears a soft, wide-brimmed hat. His smiling face rises above a flat, narrow ruff.

Pen and light brown ink on white paper; 95 × 77 mm (3¾ × 3 in.).
Signed in the upper right with the monogram: HG
References: Bartsch, Adam, *Le Peintre Graveur*, Vienna, J. V. Degen, 1803, Vol. III, pp. 40–41, No. 131 and p. 112, No. 88. Dutuit, Eugène, *Manuel de L'Amateur D'Estampes*, Paris, A. Levy, 1881, Vol. IV, p. 520, No. 7.

Comment: We are grateful to Mr. E. K. J. Reznicek, who is preparing a work of the drawings of Goltzius, for information about this drawing and for the biographical references. An anonymous early 17th-century engraving reproduces the drawing in reverse (an example is preserved in the Amsterdam Print Room). Reznicek writes[1] that he knows other examples of drawings made by Goltzius about 1600 when the artist drew in a similar free and rather coarse manner. It was probably this very freedom which caused Dutuit to hesitate in accepting the attribution. Certainly it is not a characteristic that one expects in the great Dutch mannerist engraver.

1. Letter to Agnes Mongan of 26 March 1957.

JACOB DE GHEYN II (1565 Antwerp–1629 The Hague)

22. *Head of a Young Man*

He is turned in profile to the left, looking slightly downward, his thick hair worn in short curls, a narrow ruff open at the throat.

Pen and brown ink on brown paper; 82 × 73 mm (3¼ × 2⅞ in.).
Inscribed at the lower right: De Gheyn
Collections: T. Werner (L. 2561 stamp on reverse); W. Pitcaern Knowles (L. 2643 stamp on reverse).

Comment: The young man strongly resembles the young man sketched in nine different poses on a single sheet at Berlin.[1] The Berlin page is dated 1604. In the Baer drawing the young man is a few years older and his features are, if anything, more pronounced. A companion page of almost the same dimensions (85 × 75) and inscribed in the same way by the same 18th-century hand, is in the Museum at Darmstadt.[2] Dr. van Regteren Altena has pointed out the difficulties of trying to place de Gheyn's drawings in chronological order. Although de Gheyn trained first as a glass-painter and engraver and in his later years was active as a painter, during his middle years he was chiefly a draughtsman. As Dr. van Regteren Altena records in his book, "The drawings are the binding element in his work[3] . . . Hardly one Dutch artist before Rembrandt filled his sketch-books with such a rich world of visions as he did. If as an engraver he only occasionally rises above Hendrick Goltzius, if his painting is only a modest herald of what was to be achieved later, his drawings are mature works of art, proofs of a laborious, faultless and meticulous draughtsmanship."[4] Although this drawing cannot be labeled a portrait, it is surely a study from life and one made not only by an artist of strong personal vision but one to whose hand the engraver's tools had obviously imparted a sure and strong discipline.

1. Max J. Friedländer, *Die Zeichnungen Alter Meister im Kupferstichkabinett* (Berlin: Julius Bard, 1930), p. 31, No. 2456, Tafel 23.
2. Stift und Feder, *Zeichnungen aus dem Kupferstichkabinett des Hessischen Landesmuseums zu Darmstadt*, 1929, Mappe V, VI, Darmstadt 140.
3. J. Q. Van Regteren Altena, *Jacques de Gheyn, An Introduction to the Study of his Drawings* (Amsterdam: N. V. Swets & Zeitlinger, 1935), p. 38.
4. *Ibid.*, p. 39.

LUCAS VAN UDEN (1595 Antwerp–1672 Antwerp)

23. *Recto: Landscape*

The view is of rolling country, with copses here and there, and among the trees some buildings. On the horizon of the hill in the background is a windmill.

Pen with grey-blue and yellow-green wash; 128 × 218 mm (5 1⁄16 × 8 9⁄16 in.).
Inscribed at the lower right: Van Uden

Verso: The Trunk and Lower Branches of Three Trees

Pencil.
Lightly written in pencil: "Van Uden that did the la . . ." The rest is cut away but
one can hazard the guess that it said "landscapes in paintings by Rubens."
Watermark: The letter "P" repeated with a bar uniting the two letters at the base.
Collections: Haym (L. 1970 stamp on reverse).

Comment: The drawing is one of great delicacy and sensitivity. Although
the pen line is of the finest and the transparent washes are brushed on
with a very light touch, there is a breadth of view and a sunny atmospheric effect that shows why Van Uden could and did meet Rubens' re-
quirements when he collaborated occasionally with the great Fleming in
painting the landscape backgrounds.

A drawing in the British Museum[1] with a windmill on a hill against a
stormy sky represents a similar landscape, but it is under very different
atmospheric conditions.

1. Arthur M. Hind, *Catalogue of Drawings by Dutch and Flemish Artists Preserved in the De-
partment of Prints and Drawings in the British Museum* (London: William Clowes & Sons,
Ltd., 1923), Vol. II, Plate LXXIV.

CLAES JANSZ VISSCHER
(1587 Amsterdam–1652 Amsterdam)

24. *View of the Cloveniersdoelen, Amsterdam*

A round, crenelated tower surmounted by a steeple stands at the
canal's edge in the left middle distance. At the right a path leads
across a drawbridge to a group of houses.

Pen and brown ink with grey wash on white paper; 125 × 188 mm (4 7⁄8 × 7 3⁄8 in.).
Inscribed above: 1607 Cloveniers Doelen

Comment: The attribution was first made by Miss Maria Simon of Ham-
burg. Visscher, who directed a prosperous publishing house which spe-
cialized in engraved views and maps, drew many views of canals and
buildings, often inscribing them as he has this one. In fact, a view of the
road between Haarlem and Leyden, in the Amsterdam Print Room, has
the place and the date 1607 across the sky in the same hand as the Baer

drawing.[1] Other actual views are preserved at the Louvre and École des Beaux Arts, and in the Amsterdam and Berlin Print Rooms.

A drawing of the same scene by Rembrandt was formerly in the Collection of Hofstede de Groot.[2] There is an engraved view by Jacob van Meurs (1619–80).[3] In Rembrandt's drawing the round tower, the Swijght-Utrecht Tower, lacks its steeple. The house at the left in the Rembrandt drawing and in the print (it was not yet built when Visscher made his drawing) was the Guild Hall of the Shooting Companies. It was for a company of this guild that Rembrandt, in 1642, painted the *Night Watch* which used to hang on the first floor against the wall opposite the windows.[4]

1. M.-D. Henkel, *Le Dessin Hollandais des Origines au XVII Siècle* (Paris: Les Éditions G. Van Oest, 1931), Plate xxx-b.
2. Frits Lugt, *Mit Rembrandt in Amsterdam* (Berlin: Bruno Cassirer, 1920), Plate 17.
3. *Ibid.*, Plate 18.
4. *Ibid.*, p. 30.

PAUL BRIL   (1554 Antwerp–1626 Rome)

25. *Landscape*

A turning path cut through a rocky, wooded pass descends diagonally from the upper left to the lower right. At the edge of the shadow at the lower left are two men seated, their backs turned, their dog beside them. The land falls away sharply at the right revealing a small figure looking inward across a pond towards a big tree in the middle distance, a plain and then two rocky bluffs beyond.

Pen and bistre and grey wash on white paper; 227 × 196 mm (8$\frac{15}{16}$ × 7¾ in.).
Signed and dated at the lower left: "PAVELS / 6̄6̄ / 1606."
Collections: H. S. Reitlinger.
References: Sotheby & Co. Sale Catalogue, London, June 23, 1954, No. 757.

Comment: Although Paul Bril passed by far the greater number of his productive years in Rome, where he worked first under his elder brother Matthew, who had preceded him to the Eternal City, he remained as truly a Fleming as Claude, that other adopted son of Rome whose work he was to influence so deeply, remained a Frenchman. Indeed Bril's great role is that of a link in the chain of tradition. He kept alive the particular sentiment of the Northerners for noble landscape representations, whether painted, drawn or engraved. If Patinir and Brueghel were his forebears, Claude and Poussin were his descendants. It was about 1600 that he seems to have become acquainted with Elsheimer's work and was inspired by it to such a degree that his own work was transformed. From a rather dry, thin style and an uncertain feeling for perspective, he developed a largeness of vision and a freer style more firmly founded. His trees grew to noble proportions: their structure sure, their foliage dense, the embracing atmosphere both limpid and calm. The sharply alternating diagonal areas of shadow and light visible in this drawing are characteristic of his style in the opening years of the 17th century.

The great European drawing cabinets preserve a generous selection of his drawings. Probably the most representative selection—some 40 drawings—is at the Louvre, many of them from the first decades of the 17th century. Not infrequently they are signed, as in this one, with a pair of spectacles beneath the artist's first name (in Flemish Bril means spectacles).

26. *Landscape*

A road leads from the foreground, beneath the gnarled roots of an old tree, across a single-arched bridge into the woods of the right background. The trunk of a tall tree rises in the left foreground and borders the left side of the drawing.

Pen with green, yellow and pale rose wash on white paper; 266 × 206 mm (10½ × 8¼ in.).

Comment: The drawing is neither signed nor dated, but the subtlety of the transparent washes, the easy freedom with which the foliage is drawn and the unity of the composition lead us to place it in Bril's last period, when the divisions between foreground, middle distance and background were no longer as sharp as they used to be and when his handling of an all-over atmospheric effect foretold how in later landscapes draughtsmen would use nuances of color in their washes.

HANS BOL (1534 Mechlin–1593 Amsterdam)

27. *Landscape*

At the left a road curves up from a valley; at the right, it mounts towards a village; but in the center foreground the land falls sharply away to reveal a river valley bordered by many towns on sunny hillsides until in the background the last valley is guarded by mountain ranges.

Pen and grey wash on white paper; 168 × 237 mm (6⅝ × 9⁵⁄₁₆ in.).
Signed and dated along lower right border: Hans Bol 1587
Collections: Prince Liechtenstein.

Comment: As we have said elsewhere,[1] Bol's landscapes, small in scale and lively in handling, enjoyed a great vogue even in his own lifetime.

His touch, which is rhythmical, deft and curving, reveals a temperament that is very different from that of his contemporary, Brueghel. Bol preferred a high sky line, so one generally has the impression of looking down on his scenes from a considerable height. There is a flickering light, suggested by his washes, that adds a restless movement to the air, a movement echoed in the busy little figures trudging his winding roads or working in the fields. Occasionally, as in the British Museum's *View of Antwerp*, the place can be identified. In this drawing, however, he seems to have imagined the view.

The drawing was made after he left Antwerp, but before he became a burgher of Amsterdam.

1. Agnes Mongan, *One Hundred Master Drawings* (Cambridge: Harvard University Press, 1949), p. 66.

FLEMISH, 1618

28. *Painting and Poetry*

Painting, a thin elderly man wearing a laurel wreath on his head and a loose drapery around his hips, his palette and brushes in his left hand, is sitting near a wood on a hillside with Poetry beside him. She, a rather plump young woman, also wears a laurel wreath and loose drapery. On her lap she holds a pad or oblong piece of paper or parchment. She looks up toward Painting, who gesticulates with his right hand. In the middle distance of the left background there is a castle on a hill, beyond it in the valley, a town and then mountains. The black night sky is clouded and rays of light from a hidden moon illuminate the two figures.

Dark grey prepared paper heightened with white; 146 × 191 mm (5¾ × 7½ in.).
Collections: Dr. Walter Gernsheim.

Comment: This mysterious drawing had a lengthy inscription at the lower right which someone has attempted to erase. He was not completely successful. It is possible to distinguish a few words: the first line began with a W. The tops of two more capital letters of the following erased words are still visible. The last word seems to be "Nobilus." The second line begins, "Pictor . . . prius fecit." The last, "13 December Anno 1618." Such a subject as that of Painting and Poetry talking together was favored in literary and artistic circles in the opening years of the 17th century. It has been suggested that the painter was Jan Nagel, but Nagel worked in Holland and died at Haarlem in 1616. To us this drawing has a distinctly Flemish flavor, although we can suggest no artist as author.

REMBRANDT VAN RIJN (1606 Leyden–1669 Amsterdam)

29. *The Matchmaker* (?)

In the center a woman, with a transparent veil over her head, sits near a table in profile toward the left. She appears to be listening to the proposal of the young man wearing a hat who, with arms crossed on the table, leans forward to address her.

Pen and bistre wash on white paper; 152 × 186 mm (6 × 7¼ in.).
Inscribed on reverse: Rembrand   van Rein f"
Collections: Samuel de Festetits (L. 926); J. C. Ritter van Klinkosch (L. 579); Prince Liechtenstein.
References: de Groot, Hofstede, *Die Handzeichnungen Rembrandts*, Haarlem, 1906, No. 1510; Valentiner, Wilhelm R., *Die Handzeichnungen Rembrandts*, Stuttgart, 1934, Vol. II, No. 777; Schönbrunner & Meder, *Handzeichnungen alter Meister aus der Albertina und Anderen Sammlungen*, Band IV, No. 418b; Lilienfeld, K., *Arent de Gelder*, The Hague, 1914, p. 144; Benesch, Otto, *The Drawings of Rembrandt*, London, 1954, Vol. II, p. 90, No. 397, Fig. 444; Rosenberg, Jakob, review, "Otto Benesch, 'The Drawings of Rembrandt,' " *Art Bulletin*, March, 1956, Vol. XXXVIII, No. 1, p. 69.

Comment: The subject of the drawing is only conjectural. If it represents a scene from the Old Testament, no satisfactory explanation has yet been found. Since the woman wears a veil, it is presumed that she is a widow. A noble figure, she sits in withdrawn quiet and listens to the speech of the young man whose expression has an air that is both crafty and calculating. Valentiner dated the drawing in the early forties. Benesch places it in the early thirties and describes the wash and pen lines at the right as later additions.

Dr. Rosenberg is inclined not to put it early, but to agree with Valentiner in placing it in the forties. He points out that the line is less baroque in character than it was in the early drawings and that the wash co-operates with the pen line in a way that is typical of Rembrandt's own handling. There is a tonal subtlety and transparency and a massive simplicity in the group that speaks more for Rembrandt's middle than his early period. Since the wash co-operates perfectly with the pen line to bring out the effects and has the quality of Rembrandt's wash, there seems no reason to consider it a later addition. On the shadow by the chair there was slight damage to the page. When it was restored—it is an old restoration—the wash was not touched. One can see the white edges of the old tear to prove this.

One can dismiss Lilienfeld's attribution of the drawing to Aert de Gelder as a preliminary study for the painting, *Esther and Mordecai*, at the Budapest Museum.

JAN VAN GOYEN (1596 Leyden–1656 The Hague)

30. *Scene at a River Bank*

On the broad and placid river which curves into the distance, a small sailboat and a market boat are approaching a flight of steps at the right that leads through a doorway in an old wall which seems part of an ancient ruin. Behind the wall is a round tower, with two figures on its top. A village and a windmill are silhouetted against the sky on the far bank of the river.

Black chalk and grey wash on white paper; 111 × 195 mm (4⅜ × 7⅝ in.).
Signed at the lower right with the monogram VG, dated 1652.
Watermark: The Bishop's Crook of Basle in a shield with a crown above (a somewhat later and more sophisticated version of Briquet No. 1346).

Comment: The drawing was made in the same year as the Fogg[1] Van Goyen, although the artist has used a somewhat different paper. Like others of its kind—and Van Goyen made many of these small river scenes—it is full of lively details. Van Goyen traveled widely in Holland and France, always carrying with him, it seems, his notebook, his soft black chalk and his paquette of India ink. In this particular drawing he seems to have done what Canaletto was to do so often a century later, that is, he reassembled in an imaginative composition details of an actual scene. Here he has used part of the ancient fortified wall of Nymwegen, with its round tower, crenelations and fortifications. With the addition of a windmill or with slight structural changes, he adapted the same battlements and town in paintings which are in the Collection of the Earl of Wemyss, in the Rijksmuseum, Amsterdam, in the Collection of Prince Liechtenstein, and in an English private collection.

In the drawing the small brief accents of his chalk and the grey transparent washes give this modest scene an airy, silvery quality with a charming effect of moving clouds and passing shadows. An etching needle has gone over the outlines of the drawing lightly without damaging it. This suggests that a print of the scene exists. Nagler[2] records that in 1652 there appeared a series of 13 leaves illustrating the months and showing river views with figures. It is possible that this drawing was a preliminary study for one of the etchings.

1. Agnes Mongan and Paul J. Sachs, *Drawings in the Fogg Museum of Art* (Cambridge: Harvard University Press, 1940), p. 268, No. 507, Fig. 260.
2. G. K. Nagler, *Neues allgemeines Künstler-Lexicon* ... (Munich: Verlag von E. A. Fleischmann, 1837), pp. 308–309.

SCHOOL OF REMBRANDT

31. *David Carrying the Head of Goliath*

The young David, bareheaded and clad in a tunic, his slingshot pouch suspended from a strap over his right shoulder, strides forward carrying Goliath's severed head in both hands. A bearded oriental wearing a wide turban stands behind him holding a scimitar.

Pen and bistre ink; 130 × 169 mm (5⅛ × 6⅝ in.).
Watermark: Three balls—not in Briquet.

Comment: The drawing has been attributed to Gerbrandt van den Eeckhout (1621–74), but the relationship to the very few drawings which Rembrandt specialists agree may be from Eeckhout's hand is not strong or obvious. It seems wiser, for the present, to maintain the traditional attribution to the School of Rembrandt.

JAN VAN DER CAPPELLE
(1624/5 Amsterdam–1679 Amsterdam)

32. *River Scene*

A group of three galliots and several small boats all filled with people dominates the center of the drawing. At the right is a town (Dordrecht?) with towers, steeples, and steeply graded roofs. At the left is a farmhouse at the river's edge. Birds are wheeling in the sky above the town.

Black chalk on white paper, with touches of pen on the bow of the boat in the left foreground; 208×327 mm (8⅜ × 12⅞ in.).

Comment: Although the attribution is tentative, there is good reason to believe it correct. Unfortunately almost all the 1300 drawings listed in the inventory of Van der Cappelle's effects made after his death have disappeared. There are, however, a few preserved in Amsterdam, Haarlem, Berlin and the British Museum which are similar to this drawing in their modest aim and in their style, particularly in the manner of drawing boats and in the curious calligraphy of short, curved lines which indicates figures. Like many of Van der Cappelle's paintings, most of which seem to have been done about the middle of the 17th century, he has chosen, as he did in the Frick and London National Gallery paintings, a broad river scene in a moment of calm and quiet, when the sails of the ships hang heavy in the damp air and the river's surface has only an occasional ripple of movement. Van der Cappelle, a man of inherited wealth and position, was an artist by avocation, yet a sincere and gifted one. He was also a collector, and his collection of drawings was enviable. In addition to his own portraits by Rembrandt, Hals and Eeckhout, he possessed more than 1300 landscape drawings by Simon de Vlieger, whose pupil he was, and 400 drawings by Rembrandt! The influence of the drawings of both masters is evident in this river scene.

JACOB VAN RUISDAEL   (1628 Haarlem–1682 Haarlem)

33. *The Ruined Cottage*

A thatched cottage with a tall chimney dominates the scene. The roof and walls of the section toward the spectator have fallen in, and the land around it is rough with grass weeds. Two figures are seated in the left middle distance. In the right background is another farmhouse. In front of it another figure signals with an upraised arm across a fence.

Black chalk and grey wash on white paper; 200 × 275 mm (7⅞ × 10¾ in.).
Watermark: Jester's scepter.
Collections: J. Goll von Frankenstein (L. 2987); L. Galichon (L. 1060); J. P. Heseltine (L. 1507); H. S. Reitlinger (L. 2274).
Engraved by: Ploos van Amstel.
References: Henry S. Reitlinger Collection Sale, London, Sotheby & Co., 22–23 June 1954, No. 699.

Comment: The Golls, father and son, prominent bankers of Amsterdam, had according to Lugt[1] the finest and richest collection of drawings ever assembled in Holland. There were between 5000 and 6000 pages. At the death of the grandson, the collection was dispersed in 1833. Christian Josi, an 18th-century Dutch engraver and art dealer, wrote that the 19 Ruisdaels in the Goll Collection were the finest he ever saw in private hands. The collections to which the drawing has since belonged have been scarcely less distinguished. Unlike Ruisdael's well-known paintings, with their solemn and mysterious forests of stubby and shadowy trees and gleaming pools of dark water, or the distant views of his native Haarlem with great squadrons of clouds sailing through an immense and sunlit sky, his more intimate and modest drawings are not either famous or numerous. Yet, they too, have a capacity to enclose an airy space of moving light and shadow. They are done with brief strokes of the chalk with subtle transparent washes and a few telling dark accents.

This drawing, which was probably done in the fifties, seems to have served as a preparatory study for a painting of the same subject in the Museum of Fine Arts, Boston. The changes made in the building are slight: the shape of the door, the loss of a shutter to the ruined window. The major differences are in the people. According to a tradition which seems solidly based, Wouwerman added the figures and the horse to the painting. The scene was repeated with still other figures but without the poetry of Ruisdael in a painting in the Rijksmuseum, Amsterdam (No. 1686), by Wouwerman's pupil, Emanuel Murant (1622–1700).

1. Frits Lugt, *Marques des Collections*, Supplement (The Hague: Martinus Nijhoff, 1956), p. 337.

ÉTIENNE DU PÉRAC (?) (ca. 1525 Paris–1604 Paris)

34. *View of the Tiber with the Palazzo Salviati*

The view is from a point on what is today the Lungo Tevere di San Gallo diagonally across the river so that one sees the drum of St. Peter's directly behind the Palazzo Salviati. Beyond the palace at the right is the Porta Santo Spirito. A man with a switch in his hand is driving a donkey along the path in the foreground.

Pen and ink; 160×262 mm (6⅝ × 10⅜ in.).
The drawing has been cut and mended down the center.

Comment: Du Pérac was a draughtsman, engraver and architect. He arrived in Rome from Paris in 1559 and there he remained until he returned to Paris in 1581. During his long stay he was actively associated with a publisher, Lafréry. Du Pérac's plan of ancient Rome was published in 1573. His album of 39 views of Rome was published in 1575. In 1577 appeared his bird's-eye view of Rome, which Ashby considers one of his finest works. Ashby believes that some of the drawings for the album of views were made years before the engravings were published. Two of the drawings for that publication are in the Uffizi.[1] Comparing the state of construction of St. Peter's as we can see it in Du Pérac's drawing with that shown in Dosio's drawing of 1575[2] which also shows the drum under construction, we can surmise that the Frenchman's drawing must have been made just shortly before the Dosio view. The Palazzo Salviati, now the Military Tribunal, is represented without the single bays at either end of the present façade.

Another view of the Tiber by Du Pérac, at Chatsworth, shows the river with a dredging machine at work in it. The attribution of this drawing to Du Pérac is traditional. In style it is somewhat freer than the Uffizi drawings, but that might be explained by the fact that this drawing clearly was not made to be engraved, but merely to record a scene for the draughtsman's own pleasure.

1. Thomas Ashby, *Topographical Study in Rome in 1581* (London: J. B. Nicholas and Sons, 1916). See Fig. 3, p. 22 (Uffizi 1751) and Fig. 84, p. 137 (Uffizi 1750).
2. Hermann Egger, *Römische Veduten* ... (Wien and Leipzig: F. Wolfrum & Co., 1911), Vol. I, Plate 28.

FRENCH (?) 1606

35. *A Paper Mill*

At the left is a rectangular vat with the fibers; in the middle distance, held in place by large beams, are three rows of beaters; in front of the beaters are four pumps and at the right are four more. The workmen, in jerkins, short aprons over their breeches, and brimmed hats with stiff feathers, have shovels or hoe-like instruments.

Pen and brown ink with yellow and pink wash; 117 × 250 mm (4⅝ × 8⅟₁₆ in.). Inscribed and dated at the lower left: W.W.M. 1606.

Comment: We have been unable to find any master whose name fits the initials, nor do we know of any other drawing similar to this in style, technique or subject matter. The scene is a lively one, full of acute observation and amusing detail. The yellow and rose washes give it considerable charm, but the hand is not a masterly one. The perspective is uncertain, the figures weightless. In fact, the central group are almost like figures performing a ballet. Probably the drawing was made by a provincial artist. There seems no reason to doubt either the initials or the date. Since there is something of the Second School of Fontainebleau in the character of the line, we place it tentatively in France and wonder if it represents one of the famous paper mills of the Auvergne.

CLAUDE GELLÉE, called LE LORRAIN
(1600 Chamagne, Lorraine–1682 Rome)

36. *Recto: Study of Clouds*

White cumulus clouds roll across the sky above a narrow layer of dark clouds that have still other white clouds below.

Bistre and white wash on blue paper; 95 × 200 mm (3¾ × 7⅞ in.).

Verso: Ruins

Broken fragments of capitals, plinths, and bases of columns lie scattered on a small rise of ground, silhouetted against the space beyond.

Pen.

Collections: Sir Thomas Lawrence (L. 2445); W. Esdaile (WE in ink at lower left of recto and "1836 WE" at lower left of verso—L. 2617); W. Benoni White (W stamped blind near Esdaile's mark at lower left—L. 2592).

Exhibitions: *Drawings of Old Masters*, London, Royal Academy of Arts, 1953, No. 380, p. 89.

Comment: Claude made several studies of cloud movements, choosing a blue paper and adding the white quite thickly. Some are in the Teyler Museum in Haarlem. Others are in the Berlin Print Room. They are done with a boldness and freedom that makes one think of Constable's studies of similar natural phenomena.

NICHOLAS POUSSIN
(1594 Villers, près des Andelys–1665 Rome)

37. *Landscape*

Beyond the turning road in the foreground a river in the middle distance winds into the background. The trees along the banks are reflected in the river where it bends. A path borders the river on its left bank. Two figures walk along the path in the near distance; three, in the left far distance.

Pen and brown ink, squared for enlargement in black chalk; 107 × 165 mm (4¼ × 6½ in.).
Collections: P. J. Mariette (L. 1852 stamp in center above lower edge); M. Marignane (L. 1872 stamp on reverse).

Comment: Although squared for transfer to canvas, this landscape has not been found in any specific painting of Poussin. Similar river scenes with figures walking along a river's edge occur in the backgrounds of many of his paintings. The drawing must date from Poussin's last years, for the line is summary and shaky. Its freedom and its quavering quality is that of his last style. Closest to it in handling and spirit is a drawing in the Hermitage which Friedlaender describes as "in his latest manner."[1]

The drawing is still on its Mariette mat, with a "N. Poussin" in an 18th-century hand at the lower left and on the reverse the inscription "Poussin vecchio." The 18th-century backing hides from view a letter in French which seems to be in Poussin's own hand and a decorative band of leaves and flowers. Both are visible when the drawing is held to the light.

1. Walter Friedlaender, *The Drawings of Nicholas Poussin* (London: The Warburg Institute), Vol. III, Plate 175, p. 143.

38. *Landscape with Manor*

Two twisted trees in the left and right foreground mark the beginning of an avenue lined with pollarded willows which leads towards the right distance to a small manor. A woodcutter stands chopping a log in the left foreground; farther down the avenue, a man and a woman walk towards the manor. Three dogs stand in the foreground center of the path.

Brown ink on cream-white paper; 179 × 324 mm (7 × 12¾ in.).

Comment: Various attributions have been suggested for this drawing; among them *Ercole Bazzicaluvia* (Italian engraver, working in the mid-17th century in Italy, influenced by Giulio Parigi and J. Callot), *Montcornet* (painter, engraver, picture dealer from Rouen, working in Paris ca. 1600–68), *Albert Flamen* (from Bruges, working in Paris from 1648 and best known for many engravings), *Jacques Fouquier* (b. 1590 in Antwerp, collaborated with Rubens ca. 1621 and went in 1621 to Paris where he died in 1659), *Willem van Nieulent* (1584–1635, Antwerp, Italy and Amsterdam), *Israel Silvestre* (born in Nancy, 1621, visited Italy several times, died in Paris, 1691), and *Sebastian Leclerc* (b. 1637 in Metz, died in Paris, 1714).

It has not been possible so far to identify the artist. The somewhat mannered and repetitious shading strokes are particularly characteristic of many 17th-century engravers. The manor could be Flemish or North French. The style of the building and the costumes worn by the gentleman and lady walking along the allée indicate a date in the second quarter of the 17th century. Such a date would eliminate Silvestre and Leclerc.

The arrangement of forms in perspective, with the two foreground trees resting on the lower edge, suggests the possibility that the drawing was made for a theatre set.

CLAUDE GELLÉE, called LE LORRAIN
(1600 Chamagne, Lorraine–1682 Rome)

39. *Mercury Returning to Apollo the Cattle of Admetus*

Apollo, seated on a grassy bank in front of a cliff at the left, holds his lyre in his right hand and points with his left to Mercury, who stands before him, a tall caduceus in his right hand and his winged helmet on his head. Mercury points behind, to the right, where the group of cattle are standing. In the background beyond a sunny plain are shrubs and woods and in the distance a mountain range.

Pen and brown ink with grey wash on white paper; 170×245 mm (6⅝×9⅝ in.). Signed and dated at the lower left: Claudio/inv. fecit/Roma 1671.

Comment: The scene illustrates a mythological tale of Mercury's prowess. The messenger of the gods stole 50 cows from Apollo, who when sent into exile by Zeus won through his music the post of head shepherd to the flocks of Admetus. When Apollo discovered the theft of the flocks and complained to Zeus, Mercury was ordered to return the cattle. To mollify his elder brother, Mercury is said to have given him the lyre, in return for which Apollo gave Mercury his marvelous staff, at once a herald's badge and a magician's wand.[1]

The story seems to have been a favorite one with Claude. A drawing in the *Liber Veritatis* at Chatsworth shows Mercury making off with the cattle in the left background, while Apollo, supposedly guarding the flocks, plays a lute in the center foreground.[2] The painting which the drawing records was painted for Francesco Alberici in 1655. It is now in the collection of the Earl of Leicester. A painting of *Mercury Lulling Apollo to Sleep* was painted for Bafont in 1659. A drawing in the *Liber Veritatis*[3] records the composition. An etching of 1662 repeats in reverse this latter composition. The Morgan Library has a drawing signed by Claude and dated 1663 in which Apollo sits at the right in a grove playing pipes while the cattle graze.[4] Another drawing in the *Liber Veritatis*[5] reproduced a drawing that was in the Collection of Payne Knight. It is, with a few changes, similar to the Baer drawing but in reverse. Mercury is wearing his winged sandals. Apollo grasps the lyre in both hands and the scene takes place on a steep hillside. A drawing in the Berlin Print Room[6] shows the same scene as the Baer drawing but in a larger setting, for the figures and cattle occupy only the left half of the composition and the landscape background is quite different. The Berlin drawing is also signed Claudio IV.F./Roma 1671. It is possible that some friend so admired the subject that Claude made and signed a second drawing as a gift.

The bold rhythms and the use of grey wash with the brown ink create that silvery atmosphere described by Eckhart Knab as characteristic of Claude's late drawing style.[7]

1. H. J. Rose, *A Handbook of Greek Mythology* . . . (New York: E. P. Dutton and Company, 1929), pp. 140–147.
2. Richard Earlom, *Liber Veritatis* . . . (London: Hurst, Robinson and Co., 1819), Vol. II, No. 135.
3. *Ibid.*, No. 150.
4. C. Fairfax Murray, *A Selection from the Collection of Drawings by the Old Masters* (London), reproduced No. 271.
5. Earlom, Vol. III, No. 37.
6. Reproduced by Walter Friedlaender, *Claude Lorrain* (Berlin: Verlegt Bei Paul Cassirer, 1921), p. 207.
7. Eckhart Knab, "Die Zeichnungen Claude Lorrains in der Albertina," *Alte und Neue Kunst. Wiener Kunstwissenschaftliche Blätter*, II, 1953, Part 4, pp. 121–160.

ANTOINE WATTEAU (1684 Valenciennes–1721 Paris)

40. Les Époux Mal Assortis

The procession, led by an old bearded man, moves across the page toward the left. The old man is followed by a pretty young woman attended by an elegant young man, followed by a clown strumming a guitar and a man playing a vielle. A tall tree at the right suggests a country setting.

Sanguine on paper turned tan in color; 225 × 172 mm (8⅞ × 6¾ in.).
Inscribed at the lower right: Watteau
Collections: Émile Galichon (Sale, Paris, 10–14 May 1875, No. 173); Louis Galichon (Sale, Paris, 4–9 March 1895, No. 169); Leboeuf de Mongermont (Sale, Paris, 16–19 June 1919, No. 292); Gentile di Giuseppe (Sale, Sotheby, 8 June 1955, No. 70).
Engraved by: Audran, J., *Figures de Different Caractères*, No. 302; Caylus, A. C. P., Comte de, *Œuvres de Caylus,* Paris, Cabinet des Estampes, Bibliothèque Nationale, T. I, Fol. 105, No. 32.
References: K. T. Parker and J. Mathey, *Antoine Watteau* (Paris: F. De Nobele, 1957), Vol. I, p. 20, Pl. 141.

Comment: Parker and Mathey note that the etching of the drawing by Caylus has been added to the copy of the *Figures de Different Caractères* preserved in the Bibliothèque de l'Arsénal, with the notation "On en a fait une autre." In fact, a copy of the drawing of the same dimensions was in the A. Beurdeley Collection.[1] A manuscript note by Goncourt in the copy of his catalogue of the work of Watteau at the Bibliothèque d'Art et d'Archéologie notes that the Baer drawing was in the E. Galichon sale. Louis Galichon's stamp is on the reverse of the backing to which the drawing is pasted. We give the title as it is given by Parker and Mathey. In the Beurdeley catalogue the replica is entitled *Le Ménage*

Mal Assorti, which is the title which the Baer drawing has in the catalogue of the Leboeuf de Mongermont sale.

The costumes and the composition suggest the theatre. Mme. R. Janinski and Professor Herbert Dieckmann have helped confirm this suggestion. Since the figures are small in scale and the drawing still has something of Gillot's influence evident in the character of the thin, parallel lines, Parker and Mathey list it as a youthful work.

A comedy in two acts, *Les Mal Assortis*, was presented for the first time by the Italian Comedians at the Hotel de Bourgogne on May 30, 1693. If Watteau's drawing was inspired by the Italian Comedians, and the title, which comes from the 18th century, would imply this, it could only have been this comedy. Professor Dieckmann thinks that possibly Watteau has chosen to represent a scene from Act II of that comedy. *Le Procureur* (the lawyer), the old man in elegant dress and a large beret, leads by the hand *La Coquette*, his wife. While holding her husband's left hand in her right, she gives her left hand to *Le Jeune Homme*. As they look into each other's eyes, *Pierrot* follows playing the guitar. He is followed by a man wearing a cape and playing a vielle. Professor Dieckmann points out that where Gillot was exact in his account of works on the stage, Watteau was not afraid to take liberties with the actual stage production. Here he has introduced *Pierrot* into a scene which he entered later. Watteau could, of course, have seen a production of the play in which the Italian Comedians themselves, as was their habit, took some liberties with the printed text.

1. A. Beurdeley Collection, Sixth Sale, Georges Petit, Paris, 8–10 June 1920, No. 345, reproduced.

JEAN-BAPTISTE GREUZE (1725 Tournus–1805 Paris)

41. *Study of a Woman's Left and Right Hand*

Above is a study of the right hand resting on a curved surface; below is the outstretched left hand.

Sanguine on white paper; 249 × 329 mm (9⅞ × 12¹⁵⁄₁₆ in.).

Comment: Greuze made many studies of hands: sometimes clasped, sometimes relaxed, occasionally gesticulating; dimpled, stubby and bony; hard-working hands and hands foreign to any labor. All are drawn in the sanguine he liked so much and used so often. Many are inscribed with his name. At least five such studies are preserved in the Museum of Besançon.

The hands of this drawing, like many others, seem to have been drawn more for practice and pleasure than in preparation for any particular painting.

FERDINAND VICTOR EUGÈNE DELACROIX
(1798 Charenton-Saint Maurice–1863 Bordeaux)

42. *Study for "Marphise"*

Marphisa, clad in armor, mounted on a white horse that rears on its hind legs, raises her right mailed fist above the head of Pinabel's stripped mistress, who cringes as she faces Marphisa's anger.

Brush and bistre over pencil indications on heavy ivory-white water-color paper; 228 × 225 mm (9 × 8¾ in.).
Stamp of the Delacroix sale at the lower right (L. 838).
Collections: J. W. Boehler.
Exhibitions: Ein Jahrhundert französischer Zeichnung, Berlin, Paul Cassirer, 1929–30, No. 51; *Teekeningen van Ingres tot Seurat*, Rotterdam, Museum Boymans, 1933–34, No. 58; *Französische Meister des 19. Jahrh. und van Gogh*, Bern, Kunsthalle, 1934, No. 49; *Ingres—Delacroix*, Brussels, Palais des Beaux Arts, 1936, No. 84; *Fransche Meesters uit de 19ᵉ eeuw, Teekeningen, Aquarellen, Pastels*, Amsterdam, Cassirer, 1938, No. 61; *Eugène Delacroix*, Zurich, Kunsthaus, 1939, No. 145; *Eugène Delacroix*, Bern, Kunsthalle, 1939, No. 170.

Comment: On January 6, 1852, Delacroix wrote to Andrieu, "I am up to my neck in little pictures. Having been some time without working, I have been seized with a fury for painting which I am doing on small canvases; it is simultaneously an occupation and a relaxation from large-scale works."[1] As so often happened, Delacroix chose his themes from the Bible and literature. It was at this time he painted *The Good Samaritan*, *The Disciples at Emmaus*, *Romeo and Juliet*, *A Bride of Abydos*, and composed several versions illustrating the story of Marphisa, taking his theme from Canto xx, Verse 115 of Ariosto's *Orlando Furioso*:

Marfisa incontra una gran lancia afferra,	Marfisa vincitrice della guerra
E nella vista a Pinabel l'arresta;	Fe'trarre a quella giovane la vesta,
E sì stordito lo riversa in terra,	Ed ogni altro ornamento le fe'porre,
Che tarda un'ora a rilevar la testa.	E ne fe'il tutto alla sua vecchia torre:[2]

His first essay was a charming water color which was in the Rouart Collection. It showed a spirited and pretty Marphisa mounted with the old woman on the croup behind her, Pinabel's horse rearing at the right, and Pinabel's naked mistress facing away from Marphisa's horse.[3] A second sketch eliminated both the unhorsed Pinabel and his rearing mount. A painting which belonged to Henri Delacroix (a lithograph of it by LeRoux had its stone retouched by Delacroix himself) showed the despoiled mistress turned inwards towards Marphisa.[4] The Baer drawing is not specifically recorded in Robaut, unless it was among the "Sept dessins et sepias" entitled *Marphise* listed by Robaut No. 1773, assigned to 1850. In the drawing there is no sign of Pinabel nor his horse, nor indeed of the old woman who is rewarded with the finery stripped from Pinabel's haughty and taunting young mistress. There is only an armed Marphisa, a suggestion of her rearing horse and the naked girl. Delacroix in thinking of the subject has apparently been reminded of other stories, for the movement of the horse and its rider recall his illustration of *Weislingen Attaqué par les Gens de Goetz*, a lithograph of 1836.[5]

Philip Hofer has pointed out that 40 editions of the *Orlando Furioso* appeared between 1750 and 1795: only one other period evinced a comparable interest, the Romantic Period (1822–60). During those years the poem was both read and illustrated all over Europe. It would be interesting to know if Delacroix had ever seen or heard of Fragonard's illustrations which were then in private hands in France.[6]

The drawing has often been exhibited under the title *Perseus and Andromeda*. Its present title seems the more probable.

1. Raymond Escholier, *Delacroix* (Paris: H. Floury, 1929), p. 157.
2. Lodovico Ariosto, *L'Orlando Furioso* (Paris: Presso Baudry, 1836), Vol. II, p. 253, CXV.
3. Alfred Robaut, *L'Œuvre Complet de Eugène Delacroix* (Paris: Charavay Frères Éditeurs, 1885), No. 1197, p. 321.
4. *Ibid.*, No. 1198, p. 321.
5. Loys Delteil, *Ingres & Delacroix* (Paris: Chez l'Auteur, 1908), No. 120.
6. Mongan, Hofer and Seznec, *Fragonard Drawings for Ariosto* (New York: Pantheon Books, 1945), p. 39.

JEAN-AUGUSTE-DOMINIQUE INGRES
(1780 Montauban–1867 Paris)

43. *Various Studies for "l'Apothéose de Napoleon Ier"*

In the left half, a crown of laurel; below it towards the center, a profile head of a woman with right arm holding a drapery over her head; in the right half, a more detailed study of the flying female figure with detailed studies of the right hand above and below the outstretched left arm.

Pencil heightened with white, the contours of the central figure reinforced in pen, on a rough-surfaced but very thin sand-colored paper; 225 × 423 mm (8⅞ × 16¹¹⁄₁₆ in.).

The paper is pieced at the bottom and at the lower right corner.

In Ingres's own hand with a pencil line pointing to the drapery over the right hand is the word "transparent." Below the clenched fist at the lower right is written "plus racourci" (sic!) (More fore-shortened).

Comment: The Apotheosis of Napoleon was painted in 1853 for the ceiling of the Salon of Napoleon in the Hotel de Ville. The painting was destroyed in the fire of the Commune in 1871.[1] Ingres, although he had been offered a studio in the Louvre by the Comte de Nieuwerkerke, painted the picture in a studio in the rue de Lille which was lent to him by his friend Gatteaux. It was there in February 1854 that he received the Emperor and Empress and the stream of visitors, ministers, courtiers, functionaries, critics, colleagues and the curious, whose carriages filled the street while their owners visited the studio and showered compliments on the 72-year-old artist.

Ingres had designed the painting in the shape and character of a large medallion or cameo. The scene showed a naked emperor, standing in a golden chariot drawn by four white horses. The chariot, led by *Victory*, mounts the heavens from the Island of St. Helena; *Fame* holds a civic wreath above Napoleon's laurel-wreathed head. Below at the lower left, *France* draped in mourning looks upward. From behind the vacant throne in the lower center, an angry *Nemesis* pursues *Crime* and *Anarchy*, driving them into the abyss.

The artist turned to antique coins, cameos and vases for his figures and for the shape of the chariot, the movement of the horses, the form of *Victory*. (A student, Oudine, actually made a medal after the ceiling. A reproduction in cameo was executed on the order of the government by Adolphe David after a drawing by Ingres now in the Louvre.[2]) Three preliminary sketches of the lost painting permit us to imagine its appearance: one in the Museum of the City of Paris,[3] a finished drawing with water-color washes, now in the Louvre, and a drawing without color in the Musée Bonnat, Bayonne.[4] As the Commission had stipulated, the picture was painted within a year, yet Ingres studied every detail with his accustomed care. At Montauban there are more than 80 preliminary studies. Several of them are quick pen sketches for the design of the whole composition.[5] At least a dozen are studies for the figure of Napoleon. Others are of the eagles and horses, drawings after the antique coins and after nature.[6] A splendid study for the figure of *Anarchy* was formerly in the Gatteaux Collection.[7] A study for the figure of *France* is in the Winthrop Collection, Fogg Art Museum.[8] The Fogg drawing is on the same light paper as the Baer drawing.

According to Delaborde,[9] who quotes Ingres's own explanation of the various figures, the painter was assisted by his pupils, the Balze brothers. Lapauze[10] records that R. Balze told him that he had posed several times for Ingres, that Ingres himself had posed for the figure of *Nemesis* while R. Balze designed the movement of the right arm and of the head.

The Baer drawing consists of a preliminary study of the laurel wreath which Napoleon wears and various studies of the figure of *Nemesis*, a figure which clearly harks back to the mother of the martyr in the *St. Symphorian*. In spite of Balze's story, it is difficult to see the aged artist posing for this figure, unless it is in the frown of the visage. The touches of white, so deft and telling, are clearly the master's own, as is the somewhat shaky pen line of the aging artist. The handwriting, also, even to the misspelling is unmistakably his.

The drawing has not previously been noted or published.

1. Georges Wildenstein, *Ingres* (London–New York: Phaidon Press, 1954), No. 270.

2. *Dessins et Peintures des Maîtres du XIXe Siècle à nos Jours*, Deuxième Série, Premier Volume, "Un Choix de Dessins de Jean-Dominique Ingres" (Paris: Braun & Cie, 1946), Pl. 39.

3. Wildenstein, Pl. 100, Catalogue No. 271.

4. Norman Schlenoff, *Ingres, Ses Sources Littéraires* (Paris: Presses Universitaires de France, 1956), Pl. XLVIII.

5. See Réné Longa, *Ingres Inconnu* (Paris: Librairie Rombaldi, 1942).

6. Henry Lapauze, *Les Dessins de J. A-D. Ingres du Musée Montauban* (Paris: J. E. Bulloz, 1901), p. 150.

7. Edouard Gatteaux, *Collection de 120 Dessins, Croquis et Peintures de M. Ingres* (Paris: Armand Guerinet), Series I, Pl. 21.

8. Agnes Mongan, "Drawings by Ingres in the Winthrop Collection," *Gazette des Beaux-Arts*, July 1945, pp. 387–412.

9. Henri Delaborde, *Ingres, Sa Vie, Ses Travaux, Sa Doctrine* (Paris: Henri Plon, 1870), p. 210.
10. Henry Lapauze, *Ingres, Sa Vie et Son Œuvre* (Paris: Georges Petit, 1911), p. 467.

JEAN-BAPTISTE-CAMILLE COROT
(1796 Paris–1875 Paris)

44. *Landscape with a Clump of Trees*

Young trees with gracefully curving trunks stretch their narrow branches across the page toward the lower left. In the center distance some buildings are lightly silhouetted against the sky above a wooded hillside.

Pen over pencil indications, with touches of white in the lower trunks of the trees, on tan paper; 265 × 353 mm (10⅜ × 13⅞ in.).
Inscribed in pencil at lower right in Corot's own hand, "Città Castellana, 1826."
Collection: A. Stroelin, Lausanne.
References: Gutekunst & Klipstein Sale Catalogue, Berne, Switzerland, 22 November 1956, No. 66.

Comment: Corot arrived in Rome for the first time in December 1825. He settled in a room near the Piazza di Spagna. For a while the rain kept him indoors, but soon, as he himself phrased it, "Le soleil . . . frappe sur le mur de ma chambre." Immediately he went sketching and painting in "une lumière désespérante pour moi," a light that he was never to forget. When the spring advanced he left Rome with his friend Behr to make a tour of the campagna north of Rome. He was in Città Castellana in June 1826, and again in September 1827. Since this drawing is dated 1826 and since the slender branches with tender leaves suggest spring rather than fall, the drawing was probably made on the first journey when Corot went from Città Castellana to Viterbo, Castel Sant' Elia and then to Narni. He was back in Rome in October. Over a dozen drawings made in the neighborhood of Città Castellana are listed by Robaut.[1] This drawing is not among them, but clearly it is a close companion to a drawing referred to and reproduced by Robaut.[2]

The early landscape drawings made in Rome and in the campagna have an irresistible magic. With the utmost simplicity, using a narrow pencil or pen line, in suave and sweeping rhythms the artist suggests air and light and space, wide sun-drenched panoramas or shadowy glades with rocks and quiet pools. He may have despaired of achieving the effects he sought, but no artist before or since has surpassed him at the task. In his own terms he was searching for a way to record "la force et la grace de la nature." Few artists have been more successful in recording this happy blend than the youthful Corot on his first Italian visit.

1. Alfred Robaut, *L'Œuvre de Corot* (Paris: H. Floury, 1905), Vol. IV, pp. 14–18.
2. *Ibid.*, Vol. I, Plate 35.

CAMILLE PISSARRO (1830 St. Thomas Island–1903 Paris)

45. *View of La Varenne*

The Marne flows from the left into the right middle distance. A grassy bank in the right foreground rises gently toward a thicket at the far right. On the left half is a row of poplars which is reflected in the still water of the far bank of the river; on the right background against the sky is another row of trees.

Pen and India ink over pencil on white paper; 209 × 363 mm (8¼ × 14¼ in.). *Inscribed:* "La Varenne" at lower right; signed C.P. at lower right.

Comment: On the grassy bank the artist has written in pencil "herbes," above the row of trees in the background "gris chaud," and in the sky at the right "temps chaud—ciel bleu gris chaud." Even without these notations one could surmise the colors, for the drawing magically communicates the quiet, warm stillness of an almost windless summer day. The limpid water, the few shreds of clouds, the whisper of movement in the grass and the almost palpable unifying atmosphere are in complete and quiet harmony.

Pissarro painted several views of La Varenne in 1863. La Varenne-St. Hilaire is in a bend of the river Marne. Pissarro's favorite view seems to have been from Champigny, across the river. A landscape view of La Varenne from Champigny in the Museum of Budapest[1] has the same line of trees seen silhouetted against the sky across a field.

In 1863 Pissarro exhibited with the Impressionists in the Salon des Refusés. A year later, when he showed two landscapes at the Salon, he described himself as a "pupil of Corot." Corot's influence is evident in this drawing. The Metropolitan Museum possesses a landscape drawing in pencil by Corot given by the artist to Pissarro.[2] It is interesting to observe that the gift was a drawing made in 1836 when the painter of Barbizon was still drawing with precision and exactitude, rather than freely indicating light and shadow with masses of lights and darks. Rewald might almost have been describing this drawing when, analyzing Pissarro's early style, he writes, "His [Pissarro's] work was remarkable for its restfulness, confidence, originality, firmness and delicacy of observation."

1. See Ludovic Rodo Pissarro and Lionello Venturi, *Camille Pissarro* (Paris: Paul Rosenberg, 1939), No. 31.
2. Reproduced by John Rewald, *The History of Impressionism* (New York: The Museum of Modern Art, 1946), p. 42.

AUGUSTE RODIN (1840 Paris–1917 Meudon)

46. *King Sisowat*

The bust of a Cambodian, with his chin resting on his left hand is depicted.

Pencil and crayon with chartreuse, brownish-pink and grey water-color washes; 330 × 255 mm (12⅝ × 9⅝ in.).
On the verso, not in Rodin's hand, is written "Rodin Portrait."
Collections: Roche.
Watermark: Watermark of the paper manufacturing town of Annonay (Ardèche).

Comment: In the summer of 1906 at a garden party in the Champs Élysées, Rodin saw a dance performance given by the 300 young wives of King Sisowat of Cambodia. Rodin was so excited by these strange and marvelous dancers that he invited the king to come to his home at Meudon so that he might again see the 14- and 15-year-old girls perform. It must have been a thrilling spectacle because Rodin talked of nothing else for weeks. Both while they were present and for weeks afterward he sketched the dancers incessantly.

Following the group to Marseilles, Rodin presented the king with a bronze portrait bust, which he took back to Cambodia. This drawing is probably a study for the sculpture of the king. It is a study only in a very loose sense; when Rodin was excited by a model he drew rapidly, trying with the most frugal means to catch the essence. Here he united the helter-skelter lines with a quick dash of water color, then with the addition of a few accentuating strokes of crayon, the form and a sense of the oriental potentate emerged. In this drawing, as in most of Rodin's portraits, the body has little importance. Rodin believed that great portrait busts are often bodiless; he said, "A fragment of beauty contains the whole . . ."[1] The Baer drawing unites sureness and unselfconsciousness in a most happy combination—the result of many years of effort on the part of a master draughtsman.

1. Victor Frisch and Joseph T. Shipley, *Auguste Rodin, A Bibliography* (New York: Frederick A. Stokes Co., 1939), p. 163.

PAUL GAUGUIN (1848 Paris–1903 Marquesas Islands)

47. *Recto: Page from Tahitian Notebook* (No. 15)

The head of a square-jawed oceanic man facing slightly to the left is in the upper left portion of the page.

Pencil with addition of blue and black ink; 175 × 118 mm (6½ × 4¼ in.).
The number 15, not in Gauguin's hand, is written in blue crayon at the upper right corner of the page, which seems to be the page numbering of the notebook. Number 29 is faintly indicated in pencil at the lower right corner.

Verso: Page from Tahitian Notebook (No. 15)

On the left side of the paper a seated figure with a round hat and a hank of hair falling down the back is seen from the back left side; part of the face is visible. Above is a partially drawn form, probably a back with hair, but possibly a neck and garment front opening.

Pencil and black ink; smudges of red, blue and yellow ink are on the page from page 16 recto.
Collections: Ambroise Vollard.
References: Dorival, Bernard, *Carnet de Tahiti*, 2 vols., Paris, Quatre Chemins-Éditeur, 1954, complete facsimile reproductions. In the reproductions the pages are cut. In the original drawing the line of the head of 15 recto continues. Number 15 is reproduced in black, not the original blue. There are more color spots on 15 verso coming from 16 recto than are reproduced.

Comment: When Gauguin sailed from France in April 1891 on his long-awaited voyage to Tahiti he took along a notebook which has only recently been broken up. We can determine that Gauguin must have used this book as early as the summer of 1890 and as late as the fall of 1893. On page 99 is a list of addresses. One, 54 rue Lepic, is that of Theo van Gogh before he was taken back to Holland in October 1890. Another, 12 rue Durand-Claye, is that of the Schuffeneckers in 1889 and 1890. When Gauguin returned from Tahiti he made another entry, noting expenses incurred in the fall of 1893 for the funeral at Orléans of his uncle

Isidore Gauguin ("Orléans-Chemises 150," p. 1 verso). On the boat trip out to the Pacific, Gauguin drew the portrait of a cook (2 verso), he sketched monkeys at a stop at Mahé (6 verso and 7) and a nun (97 verso) whom he met at Nouméa May 6, 1891. The sketch of the latter was used later in the painting *Soeur de Charité*.

On Gauguin's arrival in Tahiti he put down in the notebook his vivid first impressions: the huts, the dress, the picturesque aspects which must have been so striking. These first drawings, among which falls the Baer page, show primary concern for the outward form rather than the character or even body movements of the natives. Despite desperate problems of health and finances, which were so damaging to his spirit, Gauguin vigorously worked at drawing and making notes for his future use. As late as March 1892, ten months after his arrival in Tahiti, Gauguin wrote Daniel de Monfreid, "Je travaille de plus en plus mais jusqu'à présent des études seulement ou plutôt des documents qui s'accumulent— S'ils ne me servent pas plus tard ils serviront aux autres."[1] In this letter, as in those written to Monfreid on November 7, 1891 and in April 1893,[2] Gauguin told of consciously making sketches as notes to use in paintings, an interesting point, in view of the popular conception that his work was completely spontaneous. In the cuts for his books *L'Ancien Culte Mahorie* and *Noa Noa*, as well as in more than 30 paintings, we see figures from this notebook. At least the more complete figure on the verso of the Baer drawing and possibly also the one above it were incorporated into the painting *Le Diable Parle* or *La Danse du Feu*, 1891.[3] For other drawings done during his stay in Tahiti, see *Onze Menus*, edited by Robert Rey.[4]

1. Victor Segalen, *Lettres de Paul Gauguin à Georges-Daniel de Monfreid* (Paris: Éditions Georges Crès & Co., 1920), p. 86.
2. *Ibid.*, pp. 80–83 and 113–117.
3. Raymond Cogniat, *Gauguin* (Paris: Éditions Pierre Tisne, 1947), Plate 72.
4. Robert Rey, ed., *Onze Menus* (Genève: Gérald Cramer, 1950).

EDOUARD MANET (1832 Paris–1883 Paris)

48. *Mme. Edouard Manet*

On the upper left of the sheet is a three-quarter view of the head and shoulders, the head half-hidden by a hat.

Brush with black wash on graph paper lightly printed in small squares; 168×127 mm (6¾₆×4⅝ in.).

References: Duret, T., *Edouard Manet*, tr. by E. Waldmann, Berlin, Cassirer, 1910, p. 42, illustrated.

Comment: This drawing is related to Manet's painting *Portrait de Mme. Manet à Bellevue*, done in 1880.[1]

Another version of this drawing, also a wash, appears in a letter of Manet to Henri Guerard (1880).[2] It is accompanied there by another head, presumably that of Mme. Manet mère. Both sketches are referred to in the letter: "Ma mère et ma femme me chargent de leurs meilleurs compliments pour ces dames."

1. Jamot et Wildenstein, *Manet* (Paris: Editions G. Van Oest, 1932), Vol. I, No. 397, Fig. 57.
2. Moreau-Nélaton, *Manet Raconté par Lui-même* (Paris: Laurens, 1926), Vol. II, Fig. 282.

49. *Mme. Jules Guillemet*

A woman wearing a derby-type hat is seen to the shoulders; at the upper left is a woman's face turned in three-quarter view.

A light pencil sketch and a brush drawing with black wash on graph paper lightly printed in small squares; 168 × 127 mm (6¾₆ × 4⅝ in.).

Comment: The drawing is related to the pastel of 1880 *Mme. Jules Guille-met, en chapeau.*[1] It is directly related to a series of water-color drawings of the same model, standing, wearing a different attire in each new version. Two of these versions were exhibited in the Manet Exhibition of 1928 in the Matthiesen Gallery.[2]

The pointed and upturned nose, the prominent v-shaped accents of the eyes; the curling hair on the nape of the neck; the erect bearing of the head; the form of the collar and of the scarf which restricts it, and the latter's butterfly-shaped knot, the combination of the near-front view of the shoulders with a near-profile view of the head are alike in the Baer drawing and in the *Femme en Costume de Voyage.*

Both Baer drawings date from the year 1880. They are characteristic of the style of the last four years of the artist's life. During these years Manet suffered the inroads of a fatal illness in the form of paralysis of the legs—a condition which caused increasingly frequent interruptions of his work. However, his output was not diminished. He worked feverishly in his Paris studio during the winters, but his summers were plagued by the necessity of following time-consuming and immobilizing health treatments away from his beloved Paris.

In Bellevue in the summers 1879 and 1880 he continued to respond with undiminished delight and serenity to immediate visual experiences —the live source of his art throughout his career—as paintings and drawings of these years testify: they possess a heightened immediacy and simplicity of statement.

The physical handicap suffered by Manet did affect to some extent his choice of subject matter and, to a lesser degree, his choice of techniques. Pastels and water colors, which lend themselves to rapid execution, were used with increased frequency. With a new dash and verve Manet's pencil, pastel stick or brush recorded coquettish, sparkling, beribboned feminine heads as well as such trifles as the spiral of a snail on its boneless glide, or the glory of a single flower in a crystal vase. In pastels and in contemporaneous drawings, Manet exploited two very direct techniques to the same end: to characterize swiftly and brilliantly a single object which is focused on to the exclusion of other objects and of setting, and to do this with a minimum of means. Such is the aim of these two wash drawings, which as many others produced in these years, give evidence of Manet's predilection for the single object or figure isolated on the page as a vignette. Many of Manet's favored motifs of these years, or rather the unique images in which he cast them graphically, are found in a number of distinct drawings executed in different media, each involving no essential transformations of the initial vision and concept. This is the case with these two heads which can be related to oils and to other wash drawings. These related versions of the same motif do not represent preparatory stages in the elaboration of a final and complete version —as is often the case among drawings of draughtsmen such as Ingres or Degas—but each is a self-sufficient image and simply restates an essentially fixed arrangement of spots and lines characterizing Manet's initial visual experience of the model.

Manet's deft and bold handling of the brush gives to the two heads an appearance of casualness which would suggest that they were sketched directly from their respective models. However, the evidence of related works (listed under each title), identical in basic form and content, and differing only in media, casts some doubt as to whether these drawings represent initial recordings of their subjects. In any case, the related works point to Manet's ability to recapture in each new image the excited spontaneity transmitted initially to a first sketch.

1. Jamot et Wildenstein, *Manet* (Paris: Editions G. Van Oest, 1932), Vol. I, No. 430, Fig. 223.
2. *Manet*, February-March 1928, Berlin Matthiesen Gallery, Catalogue Nos. 65 and 66. *Femme en Costume de Voyage* is illustrated in Plate LXIII and *Femme en Costume de Bain*, in Plate LXIV.

HENRI de TOULOUSE LAUTREC
(1864 Albi–1901 Céleyran)

50. *Recto: Study of a Monkey*

A monkey, sprawled on its back, is playing with its feet in the air.

Pencil on white paper; 157 × 256 mm (6⅜ × 10⅛ in.).
Inscription: Signed with monogram at the right; there is a red stamp at the lower left; inscribed 1880 at the lower left.

Verso: Two Sketches of a Woman's Head

At the center is a head turned in profile toward the left; to the left of it is a slight sketch of a forehead and nose, while to the right and a little below is the head of a woman facing front and wearing a headdress and a blouse with a ruff.

There is a monogram between the two heads.
Collections: G. Pellet; Maurice Exsteens.
Exhibitions: Galerie Thannhauser, Paris, 1938; Weyhe Gallery, New York, Toulouse Lautrec Exhibition, 1943.
References: Joyant, Maurice, *Henri de Toulouse Lautrec, Dessins-Estampes-Affiches*, Vol. II, Paris, H. Floury, Ed., 1927, p. 180; Parke-Bernet Galleries, April 12, 1945, No. 40, illustrated.

Comment: In 1875 at the age of eleven, Lautrec was drawing and working with René Princeteau, a friend of the Lautrec family and a painter of animals. The two disastrous falls, in 1878 and 1879, which left Lautrec a cripple, certainly also brought to the forefront the artistic interest which he had manifested previously. A sketch book in the Chicago Art Institute, dated 1880,[1] and another book in the Boston Public Library, a collection of drawings of about this period,[2] give further examples of the young artist's inclinations. These books include mainly drawings of horses and sailors seen at Nice where he was convalescing. The Chicago sketch book is of almost the same dimensions (6⅝₆×10¼ in.) as this page. In these two books and in the drawing of the monkey, which is also on a page torn from a sketchbook (as one rough edge proves), there is already manifested a keenness of observation and a wit which one associates with Lautrec's mature work. The paws are a bit unsure, but in the drawing of the head and the position in which the young artist catches the animal, one sees a knowledge and individuality remarkable for a boy of sixteen.

1. Carl O. Schniewind, *A Sketch Book by Toulouse-Lautrec owned by the Art Institute of Chicago* (New York: Curt Valentin, 1952).
2. Arthur W. Heintzelman and M. Roland O. Heintzelman, *H. de Toulouse Lautrec, One Hundred Ten Unpublished Drawings* (Boston: Boston Book and Art Shop, 1955).

PAUL CÉZANNE
(1839 Aix-en-Provence–1906 Aix-en-Provence)

51. *Recto: The Unmade Bed*

The curving metal forms at the head of a single bed are pushed close to a window. The rumpled covers dominate the foreground.

Graphite pencil on white paper; 270×210 mm (10¾ × 8¼ in.).
The drawing is numbered LXV at the upper right.

Verso: Drapery Sketch

The page is numbered LXVI.

Collections: Paul Guillaume; Adrien Chappuis; A. Stroelin.
References: A. Chappuis, *Dessins de Paul Cézanne* (Paris, 1938), Plate 41; A. Venturi, *Cézanne, Son Art, Son Œuvre* (Paris, 1936), Vol. I, p. 313; Stroelin sale, Gutekunst & Klipstein, Berne, 22 November 1956, No. 60, Tafel 30.

Comment: Theodore Reff[1] believes on the basis of the handling of line and the organization of the picture surface that Cézanne made the drawing between 1880 and 1882. He places it close to the drawing reproduced by Rewald[2] which he demonstrated to be of 1882.[3] The motif, he notes, is typical of Cézanne especially in the early eighties: a sequence of overlapping planes parallel to the picture plane, forming a sequence of screens as it were. The severe rectilinear organization of the surface is also typical of the period. There are areas of tone, formed by rapid diagonal shading with accents made by thin, dark, incisive lines, often repeated at the contours. It lacks the purity and restraint of drawings done in the later eighties and nineties, but it is most interesting for the conception of the motif.

1. Letter to Agnes Mongan, 28 October 1957.
2. John Rewald, *Carnets de Dessins de Cézanne* (Paris, 1951), Plate 45.
3. Theodore Reff, "Two Cézanne Drawings," lecture given at the Frick Symposium, New York, 6 April 1957.

HENRI MATISSE (1869 Le Cateau-Cambrésis–1954 Nice)

52. *Bust of a Young Woman*

She is leaning on her right elbow, bending slightly towards the spectator.

Pen and black ink on white paper; 366 × 267 mm (14⅜ × 10½ in.).
Signed at lower right: Henri Matisse

Comment: The similarities of style, costume, and model to those in a series of drawings which Matisse executed in Nice in 1919 make it most probable that this drawing bears the same date.[1] The group offers rich material for understanding Matisse, the draughtsman. The artist working from one or two models finds a remarkably rich and varied source of inspiration. His analyses of the models lead not to more exact likenesses, nor do they end in abstract notation. Instead, they uncover a never-ending progression of interpretations. The expression of the model changes before our eyes as Matisse seizes upon each new aspect of his sitter's countenance or mood. The content is also transmuted as the pen or pencil strokes change from tight, elegant rendition to sketchy informality. Yet the models tend to remain comparatively passive. Since, in each study, the artist uses a restricted linear vocabulary, the artistic means remain unified and uncomplicated.

This drawing seems to catch and exploit a characteristic of the model which Matisse noted in other studies of the same girl. She engages the spectator with her wide-open, arched, right eye, while almost at a different moment, she looks through or beyond us with her more precisely defined left. As we feel the differences in her eyes, the whole face comes into plastic existence. The mouth, too, is slightly asymmetrical, while the heaviness and solidity of her right cheek contrasts with the tentative

64

softness and incompleteness of her left. This ellipsis of line, so necessary to artists like Matisse and Picasso, here helps to separate the large planes of arm and face by uniting the latter with the background. The spatial progression thus created not only accentuates the forward inclination of the model, increasing the sense of intimacy, but sets off the pattern of the dress. A concern with pattern and with the very texture of line itself is one of the delightful aspects of the drawing. There is the utmost unity and economy of the expressive means and the content expressed.

1. Cf. Henri Matisse, ed., *Cinquante Dessins par Henri-Matisse* (Paris: Vildrac, 1920).

PABLO PICASSO (1881 Malaga–

53. *Sketches of Six Circus Horses, Some with Riders*

Four of the six horses have bareback riders who are putting the horses through different paces. At the top is a head and neck of a horse, and in the lower right center a horse is being led.

Pen and ink; 247 × 327 mm (9¾ × 12⅞ in.).
Signed in a different ink at the lower left: Picasso[1]
Collections: Leo Stein; Henry Kleemann; acquired through Curt Valentin.
Exhibitions: The Art Museum, Princeton University, *Picasso Drawings,* January 1949, No. 4; State University of Iowa, *Six Centuries of Master Drawings,* 1951, No. 212; Wesleyan University, Middletown, Connecticut, *Symposium of the Graphic Arts,* 1955.

Comment: This early drawing, which on both external and internal evidence can be dated 1905, shows the artist as a draughtsman of supreme sensitivity at the age of twenty-four. It is related to the dry point *At the Circus,*[2] the oil *The Watering Place,* the charcoal drawing the *Boy on a Horse,*[3] as well as to the pen and ink studies of similar size, the *Figures and Bulls,*[4] *Figures* and perhaps also the *Leo Stein.*[5] All of these were made in 1905.

Although the motifs are not arranged as a connected scene or narrative, there are subtle balances of opposing movement in space and the figures are further unified by the remarkable grace of execution and the merest suggestions of form. The lower right figure on horseback, Picasso repeated in the middle of *The Watering Place.* In thin pen strokes Picasso creates figures of astonishing plastic existence and a mood that is witty, gay and graceful.

1. The signature was added by Picasso in 1948 at the request of Curt Valentin.
2. Alfred H. Barr, Jr., *Picasso: Fifty Years of His Art* (New York: The Museum of Modern Art, 1956), p. 40.
3. *Ibid.*, p. 42.
4. Alfred H. Barr, Jr., ed., *Picasso, 75th Anniversary Exhibition* (New York: The Museum of Modern Art, 1957), p. 25.
5. *Picasso Drawings* (a catalogue) (Princeton University: The Art Museum, 1949), No. 5 and No. 11.

54. *Two Bearded Men Looking at a Giant Bust of a Woman's Head*

Two bearded men, wearing only trunks, stand at the right viewing the bust at the left; the one nearer the bust has his arms folded, the one behind him at the right points toward the bust with his outstretched right arm.

Pencil on heavy white paper; 329 × 261 mm (12$\frac{15}{16}$ × 10¼ in.).
Signed at the lower left: Picasso Paris le 27 novembre XXXI

Comment: In 1927 Picasso took up a theme that was to fascinate him for the next seven years: the artist (sculptor or painter) in his studio, often with his model. In 1930 the theme was used to illustrate Balzac's *Le chef-d'œuvre inconnu*.[1] In 1933, after Picasso had acquired his sculptor's studio at Boisgeloup, it was expanded into 46 of the 100 plates for the *Vollard Suite*.[2] This drawing, dated 1931, is in its great economy stylistically close to the etchings of 1931 for Ovid's *Métamorphoses*.[3]

Picasso's graphic production of the early thirties was largely tied to literary illustration, and a point of extreme facility was attained. His flowing plastic line which creates long, unbroken contours carried on the art of the Greek vase painters and the tradition of Raphael and Ingres. It is not merely a virtuoso performance.

Although the literary aspect of the drawing is not specific, one feels that Picasso is paying homage to a source of his art. As Picasso himself often is, the observers are clad only in shorts. Does the contrast of their bearded faces with the refinement of the sculpture intimate that it is the classic that refines, or at least balances, the Dionysiac? The two react differently to the bust: one is actively inspired, the other, restrained and contemplative. Their reactions are emphasized by their relation to the background demarcations. The two vertical lines, so often included by

Picasso to suggest spatial setting, are broken and exceeded by the active figure, but just ever-so-nearly approached by the outline of the passive artist. The finesse and suggestiveness of these details is part of the astonishing power and ease of Picasso's draughtsmanship, which makes his graphic work rank with the best of all times.

1. Honoré Balzac, *Le chef-d'œuvre inconnu* (Paris: Ambroise Vollard, 1931). The edition contains 13 original etchings and 67 woodcut reproductions of Picasso's drawings.
2. *Picasso's Vollard Suite*, introduction by Hans Bolliger, translated by N. Guterman (London: Thames & Hudson, 1956).
3. Ovid, *Les Métamorphoses* (Lausanne: Albert Skira, 1931).

GERMAN, EARLY 16TH CENTURY

55. *Sketches of German Medieval Castles*

Medieval towers and buildings, perched on hills, are seen from below.

Pen and black ink; 181 × 291 mm (7⅛ × 11⁷⁄₁₆ in.).
Watermark: A high crown—close to Briquet No. 4952—indicates that the paper is German.
A large water stain covers the top of the drawing. There are spots throughout the page.
Collections: Prince Liechtenstein.

Comment: These studies of five clusters of medieval buildings create a charming page. The quick and delightful calligraphic strokes which form the hills and vegetation are so airy that the effect becomes that of a fairy-tale illustration rather than architectural studies of massive fortresses. The drawing is clearly in the early 16th-century German tradition. The fact that the paper seems to be of Augsburg origin is suggestive of a location. Professor Winkler has pointed out the similarity between this drawing and the architectural part of *Sketch Leaf with Landscape & Animals*, formerly in the Pembroke Collection.[1] However, a lack of sureness in the relation of one plane to another in this drawing rather points away from the two being by the same artist.

1. Friedrich Winkler, *Die Zeichnungen Albrecht Dürers* (Berlin: Deutscher Verein für Kunstwissenschaft, 1936), Vol. I, Pl. XXIII.

SCHOOL OF NIKLAUS MANUEL, called DEUTSCH
(ca. 1484–1530 Bern)

56. Recto: St. Barbara in a Landscape

She is standing facing left between two trees in a country clearing, draped in the full folds of her gown, her hair caught up in an elaborate coiffure with a halo. Her head is in profile and her body is turned slightly toward the viewer. She holds the sacramental cup in her left hand and its cover, roughly inscribed with the adored crucifix, in her raised right hand. The clearing is protected by a paling from the outside world of a town at the right; a tower crowns a hill at the left. In the background are distant mountains. A small dog lies curled in the center foreground.

Pen and black ink; 147 × 107 mm (5¹³⁄₁₆ × 4³⁄₁₆ in.).
Inscribed at top center 1515 and at lower left (perhaps in later ink) GV (or GU). A narrow strip of paper reinforces the page at the right where it had frayed.

Verso: Nude Woman with Flying Drapery

She stands in a frontal view, on the right upper half of the page, appearing to be placed on a rock, perhaps in a lake, with the suggestion of a town across it at the right. A scarf passes from her right hand through her legs and swirls over her head.

Black chalk; 147 × 107 mm (5¹³⁄₁₆ × 4³⁄₁₆ in.).
Part of the top of the page is covered with paper used to restore the recto.
Collections: Prince Liechtenstein.

Comment: While the fully depicted landscape at first suggests a drawing of the Danube School, the emphasis on a single, large figure elaborately dressed and coiffed seems to place it rather in the Swiss School. The forward slouching figure of the saint recalls the Gothic sway of St. Barbara in Niklaus Manuel's 1515 Grandson altarpiece—as do the petal design of the base of the cup and the spiked effect of the hair (or head covering). The sharp profile of the face and the curve of the posture are close also to Manuel's drawings of this same date, although his figures are less attenuated, more Italianate.

This St. Barbara, if it is St. Barbara as the tower suggests, lacks the certainty and boldness of line of Manuel's figures. More significantly, it lacks his often whimsical, contemporary commentary. These weaknesses as well as the nude woman (verso) whose composition is similar to some as yet unanalyzed sketches in Manuel's drawings in Basel suggest that the drawing is from his Bern workshop, from 1512 to 1523.

The monogram is not one that is known.

GERMAN OR AUSTRIAN (?) 18TH CENTURY

57. *Recto: Music-making Angels*

At the left, seated on the edge of a coping with the left leg hanging over the edge and looking down toward the left, is an angel, with great wings, strumming a lute. At the right, also seated near the edge, is another angel looking up and playing a viola da gamba. Lightly sketched below, left center, are two other angels: the one at the left is playing a small portable organ, the one at the center is playing a harp. At the right two small *putti* support a candelabrum with three candles.

Black chalk, pen, brown and grey wash; 390×250 mm (15⅜×9⅞ in.).

Verso: There are two roundels, one with sketches for a martyrdom of a bearded Franciscan saint, the other with the saint presenting a child to a kneeling woman.

Black chalk.

Comment: Although the drawing has a strong personal flavor, it has not yet been possible to attribute it to any of the well-known Austrian and German decorators of the 18th century. The mixture of influences—the Roman flavor in the rounded contours and the largeness of the features and forms, which seem to descend from Conca and Pietro da Cortona, and the handling of brilliant modelling through light and shadow which recalls Tiepolo—speak of Italy. Yet in the weightlessness of the large figures, the play of light and shadow over the full folds of drapery, and the summary drawing of fingers and feet, there is clearly something of the North. The author must have been an artist such as Gregorio Guglielmo, who worked in Rome, Dresden, Vienna, Turin, Berlin, Augsburg, Warsaw and Petersburg in the middle years of the 18th century. Guglielmo's ceiling frescoes at Schönbrunn and a chalk drawing of the male nude in the Uffizi[1] are not too different in feeling and handling.

The Bergamesque painter Giuseppe Antonio Felice Orelli (1706–76), who was an assistant of Tiepolo in Venice and who later worked in several towns of the Italian lake region, painted for the Collegiata of St. Pietro e Stefano in Bellinzona some music-making angels that are not too different from those of this drawing. A solution of the problem of attribution cannot be reached without further study.

1. Gernsheim, No. 10059.

GERHARD MARCKS (1889 Berlin–

58. *Seated Male Youth*

He is shown facing and gazing out to our left, in a seated posture without any background. Both legs are drawn up so that the right hand rests on the right knee and the left forearm is supported by the left knee.

Pencil on white paper; 458 × 305 mm (18 × 12 in.).
Signed at the lower right of the figure: G. Marcks. Stamped on the lower right of the sheet is "MADE IN GERMANY."

Comment: Marcks' sculptural works neither exude joy nor manifest inner compulsion; usually nudes, they are neither sensuous declarations nor are they expressionistic distortions. Thus the stylistic position of Marcks has been established between that of Maillol and Lehmbruck, on the one hand, and Barlach on the other. Yet, the restraint and simplicity of this artist's work seem to be archaic when they are opposed to either the formal or symbolic sophistication of the others. There is a geometric austerity to Marcks which, together with his predominant interest in the single, inactive figure, surrounds each work with a self-contained quiet.

Most of Marcks' drawings, especially those of the forties and fifties, are from models. They often appear in poses that do not imply any external psychological or physical relationships. Although the masses are usually not closed, and space is rarely excluded, the sense of isolation is never sacrificed. The character of many of these quick and somewhat impersonal studies is partially geometric. In this drawing the face, arms, and back are near-silhouettes. As in a great many of the sculptures, there are distinct but subtle planes that compose legs and arms. Perhaps this formal simplification results from Marcks' former association with the *Bauhaus* in 1920–25. The pencil line has a feeling for the continuous flow of contour. This imparts not only relaxation but also weight to the figure. It is not the curvilinear abandonment of Rodin's line, nor the fullness of Maillol's, just as it is not the remarkable plastic line of Picasso. It has instead a slight awkwardness that is Germanic in character. Contours do not quite work together to model full volumes nor do they have the feeling of elasticity that would often define the limit of a flexing muscle. This peculiar inorganic nuance of the drawn figures and the sculptures not only is Marcks' personal idiom, but it is the very thing that removes these otherwise natural-looking figures from the sphere of ordinary observation.

ERNST BARLACH (1870 Wedel–1938 Guestrow)

59. *Two Huntsmen with a Dog, Walking in the Moonlight*

The two men are at the right, looking back over their shoulders, while making their way through a valley landscape lit by the moon at the upper left.

Brush and sepia gone over with charcoal; some white chalk and preliminary sketching in pencil; 241 × 335 mm (9⅞₆ × 13¼ in.).
Signed at the lower left: Barlach Florenz 1909
Watermark: P. M. Fabriano.

Comment: The re-emergence of German sculpture to the highest rank began with the coming to maturity of Ernst Barlach during the first decade of this century. Like other modern artists such as Matisse and Munch, he was slow to develop his personal style. Like Kandinsky and Kokoschka, he was very active as a writer. Further, Barlach was a prolific and sometimes powerful illustrator in both woodcuts and lithographs. Coming into his own after 1906, Barlach reacted against the sentimental superficiality of *Jugendstil* and the realism of much contemporary German sculpture. He created an art combining monumental plastic simplicity with a unique expression of sympathy for humanity. The manifest source for these qualities was his discovery of the Russian peasant during his travels of 1906.

By 1909, the date of this drawing, Barlach's style had moved further away from the decorative, although his sculpture would often display a beautifully carved surface. Continuing his personal aversion to the nude,

Barlach invariably worked with ponderous, depersonalized draped figures, undoubtedly inspired in part by the sculpture of the Middle Ages. The draped figure enabled Barlach to avoid the exigencies of anatomical logic. It lent itself to a distortion of movement and an intensification of formal contrasts which are so much a part of the expressionist's vocabulary.

Although the source of the drawing is not known, it is illustrative in character. Were it not for the peasant's rather intense glance over his shoulder, the composition would be unbalanced. It is a moonlit night, perhaps reminiscent of the Florentine hills, and there is a possible connection with Theodore Däubler's *Nordlicht*, since Däubler and Barlach were in Florence together.[1] Yet the style and dress of the figures still recall those of Barlach's Russian sketches. The rugged faces, the crude caps, the sack-like clothing reducing the bodies to basic shapes, and the clumsy, heavy feet (bearing an unexpected similarity to some peasants drawn by Camille Pissarro) combine to intensify the basic concern of the figures. The landscape is drawn in repeated strokes that may derive from Van Gogh, but the line is quite overworked. The tendency to use a heavy touch and to define and hatch with a curled line is peculiar to Barlach's graphic works, whether drawings or prints. The style of this drawing is transitional. It looks forward to the less spacious and more angular illustrations which followed it.

1. Naomi Jackson, "Ernst Barlach: Gothick Modern," *Art News* LIV (December 1955), 38 ff.

MAX BECKMANN (1884 Leipzig–1950 New York City)

60. *Bird Play*

To the right, seated on rocks, are three females, semi-nude, with large limbs, small heads, and streaming hair. At the left, four large birdlike creatures seem to be performing, attracting the attention of the females with their jaunty postures. In the background is a mountain range with a smouldering volcano.

Pen and india ink on white paper; 445 × 583 mm (17½ × 22⅚ in.).
Signed at the lower left: Beckmann Boulder 49.
Collections: Mrs. Beckmann.
Exhibitions: Six Centuries of Master Drawings, State University of Iowa, 1951, No. 156.

Comment: It is with great difficulty that the disquieting effect of the content and execution of this drawing is dispersed. It is not too far from the truth to declare this intentional. For, from the twenties on, Beckmann rarely made concessions to rhythmical outline and logically built space. It was only in his portraits that the rough edge of the irrational was smoothed over. And yet, after sufficient time, one does realize that there is satire and humor instead of pure horror and ugliness, and that the graphic means provide a satisfying unity.

The drawing, entitled *Vogelspiel* by Beckmann, was executed during the summer of 1949 (actually completed on August 17, 1949) when Beckmann was conducting an art class in Boulder, Colorado. His time was divided among teaching, walking, touring, and such entertainment as the rodeo and the movies; there was little work accomplished with the exception of about 11 finished drawings. We read in the diaries of visits to "Vesuv" and to the great dinosaurs of the Natural History Museum in Denver, of climbing the red rocks and visiting the open amphitheatre near Boulder, and of the great heat and constant thunderstorms.[1] An impression of elemental nature certainly is reflected in our drawing. In the landscape and in the crudely articulated figures there is a definite primeval quality which contrasts with the obvious sophistication of the artist's message.

That the birds are performing and the women are reacting is clear. There is nothing sinister about these birds; to the contrary, there is humor in their inflated pride and self-esteem. The women watch the performance seriously. The near figure claps in enjoyment; the middle woman is quite entranced and fixed, as is shown by her block-like torso and her raised finger; while the third lady is awe-inspired, raising her hand to her head in profound amazement. In the contrast between the genuineness of the women's reaction and the mock-acting of the birds, we, the spectators of the whole show, begin to feel the satire intended. This is not the incisive, specifically social satire of the *Neue Sachlichkeit* of the twenties, but one less specific, more universally applicable, and deepened by a sense of the comic.

Looking back through Beckmann's works we often find the bird, man-sized and with large beak; examples are in the *Departure* of 1932–35, the *Temptation* of 1936, the *Perseus* of 1941, the *Bird's Hell* of 1947, and others. Although one rightly has trepidations in finding exact symbolic references for Beckmann's birds (as well as for his ubiquitous fish, bell boys, kings, etc.), there is the possibility of generalizing. The birds are almost men in stature and in action; and their task seems to be a mimicking of the unenlightened ways of man. In this drawing they charm the huge, unthinking women, whose small heads, huge bodies and primitive dress also suggest a lack of intelligence. The long hair, paralleling the fumes from the distant volcano (besides being graphically humorous), suggests a wind force. Finally, off to the left, the diminutive seated figure and the standing bird indicate the vast space portrayed, emphasizing the foreground scene and its fantastic scale. The whole bird-play, then, is an imaginative representation of the frivolous and unreal preoccupations of man, with a non-specific suggestion that his basic physical nature may be responsible.

The drawing is held together by a thick, boldly applied line which is supported by the finer spun line of internal texture. It is interesting that the women are rendered with rougher surface than are the birds. In any case, there is no attempt to portray the scene with specific texture or to represent natural accidents such as lighting. The entire treatment subserves the imaginative world.

1. Max Beckmann, *Tagebücher 1940–1950* (Munich: Langen und Müller Verlag, 1955), See pp. 322–334.

OSKAR KOKOSCHKA

(1886 Pöchlarn, Austria, on the Danube–

61. *Head and Shoulders of a Woman*

> She is seen slightly from below, glancing to her right, with her left arm raised so that her hand lies on top of her head.

Red chalk; 445 × 310 mm (17⁹⁄₁₆ × 12³⁄₁₆ in.).
Signed lower right: OKokoschka
Collector's stamp on upper left verso is unrecognizable.

Comment: In 1931 Kokoschka returned to Vienna where he had begun his career. The next three years brought him recognition and success, and a corresponding easing of the artistic exploration that had characterized his European travels of the twenties.

It was about 1931[1] that a series of twenty red chalk drawings of Mrs.

M. was executed. It seems probable that this drawing belongs to the series. The group has not the depth of mood or psychological penetration offered by the superb *Variations on a Theme* of 1920,[2] where the model is metamorphosed by her reactions to the music she hears. Rather, the primary intention of the Mrs. M. series seems to be portraiture, even likeness, as from sheet to sheet the features of Mrs. M.'s face maintain a rigorous similarity. In contrast to the 1920 works, the model does not remain quite so removed from our psychological sphere. As Kokoschka may have been attracted by the sensuous appeal hidden behind this not too ingratiating face, the drawing is imbued with a personal quality which brings the spectator into sharp interaction with the sitter.

As a portrait, the drawing confronts us with a haughty, Slavic countenance, whose aloofness is nearly sphinx-like. As in many of the other studies of Mrs. M., a smug effect is created by enclosing the undefined cheeks and jowls in an imprecise shell of heavy strokes. The features, which seem almost pasted on, are rendered with light lines. The face is an image that emerges through a layer of the most casual drawing.

A comparison of this apparently careless drawing with the clean line of, for example, a Matisse drawing helps to clarify important differences. Whereas the linear vocabulary selected by Matisse is inextricably bound to the content, the graphic means of Kokoschka serve two levels of meaning. For not only is the impassive attitude of the sitter re-enforced by the apparent lassitude of the line, but the execution of the line itself cries out for independent recognition. This independence of the means is really an insertion of the artist's creative self into the work of art; we not only recognize the artist's style, but we are forced to acknowledge his presence. It is not only the distortion of nature, but it is the distortion of the graphic conventions upon which the Expressionist insists. And now, following World War II, the Abstract Expressionists have demonstrated the validity of this second level.

---

1. Edith Hoffmann, *Kokoschka, Life and Work* (London: Faber and Faber, 1947), p. 330.
2. Originally drawings; then issued as original signed lithographs and subsequently in excellent collotype reproductions.

2. Florentine, ca. 1460
*Standing Draped Figure
Seen from the Back*

1. Titian (?)   *Two Satyrs in a Landscape*

3. Passerotti *Sketches*

4. Circle of Zuccaro *Moses, Aaron & Hur at the Battle of Israel & Amalek*

5. Guercino *Esther and Ahasuerus*

6. Guercino *Landscape with Bridge and Figures*

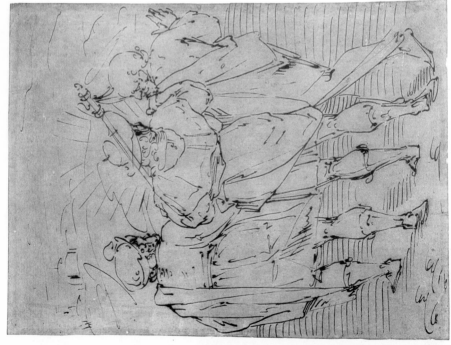

10. Rosa   *Two Men Discover the Body of a Third Man*

9. Tiepolo   *Figure of a Man*

11. Piazzetta   *A Young Man Embracing a Girl*

12. Murillo *St. Joseph and the Young Christ*

13. Master of the Tobit Legend *Jacob's Dream*

14. Swiss Master(?), 16th Century   *Group of Nude Figures*

15. Heemskerck   *Triumph of Job*

16. Heemskerck (?)   *Roman Landscape*

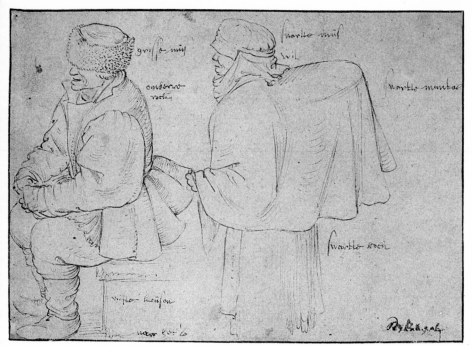

17. Pieter Brueghel, the Elder   *Studies of Peasants: Recto*

18. Pieter Brueghel, the Elder   *Studies of Peasants: Verso*

19. Mabuse   *Old Testament Scene* (?)

20. Abraham Bloemaert *Adam and Eve*

21. Goltzius *Head of a Young Gentleman*

22. Jacob de Gheyn II *Head of a Young Man*

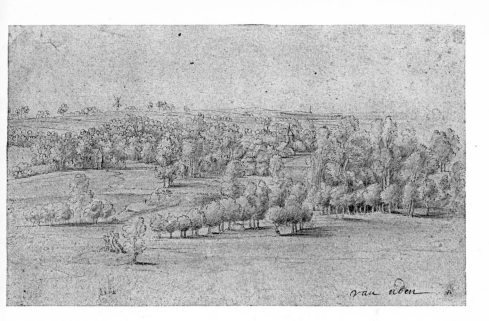

23. Van Uden *Landscape*

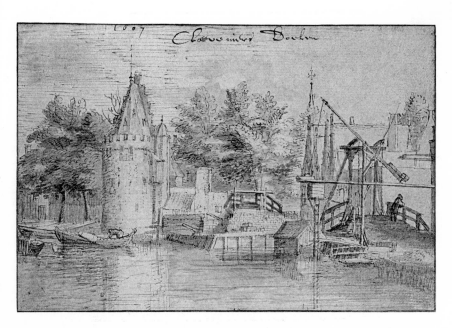

24. Claes J. Visscher *View of the Cloveniersdoelen, Amsterdam*

25. Paul Bril *Landscape*

26. Paul Bril *Landscape*

28. Flemish, 1618 *Painting and Poetry*

30. Van Goyen *Scene at a River Bank*

31. School of Rembrandt *David Carrying the Head of Goliath*

32. Van der Cappelle *River Scene*

33 · Jacob Van Ruisdael   *The Ruined Cottage*

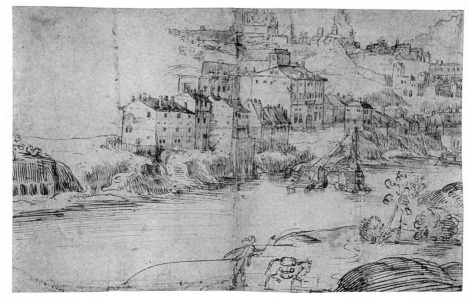

34. Du Perac (?)   *A View of the Tiber with the Palazzo Salviati*

35. French?   *Papermill, 1606*

36. Claude *Study of Clouds*

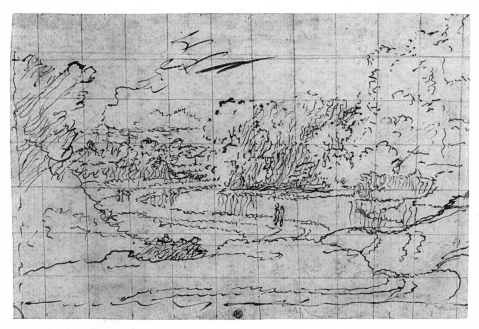

37. Poussin *Landscape*

38. Flemish, 17th Century *Landscape with Manor*

39. Claude *Mercury Returning to Apollo the Cattle of Admetus*

40. Watteau *Les Époux Mal Assortis*

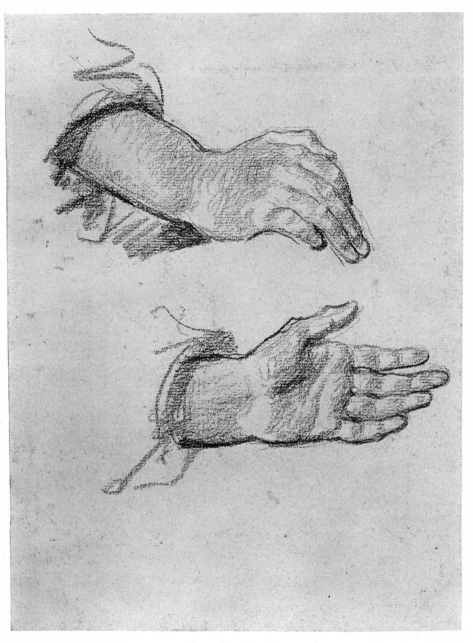

41. Greuze   *Study of a Woman's Left and Right Hand*

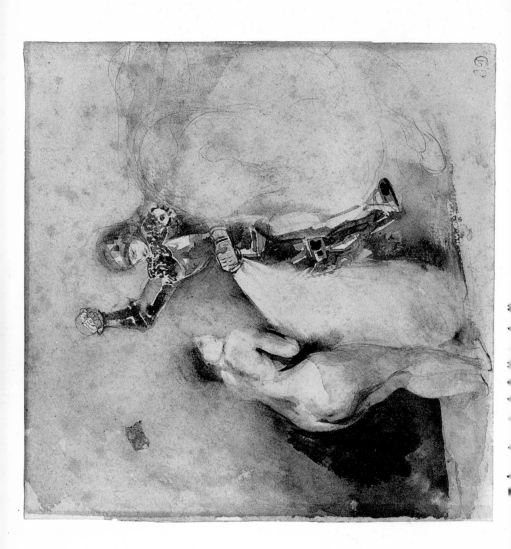

43. Ingres *Various Studies for "l'Apothéose de Napoleon Ier"*

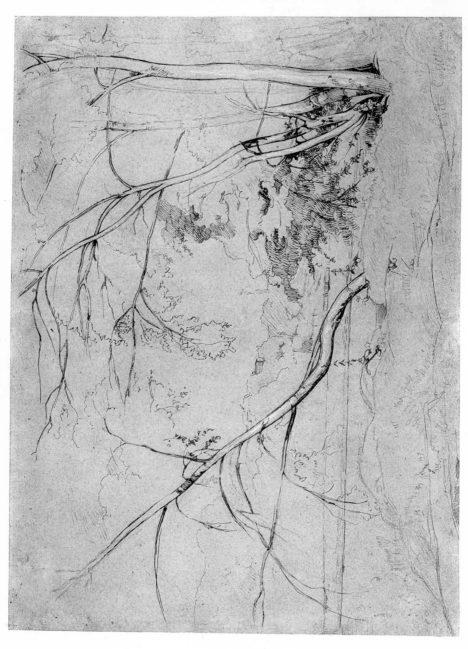

44. Corot *Landscape with a Clump of Trees*

45. Pissarro *View of La Varenne*

46. Rodin *King Sisowat*

47. Gauguin *Page from Tahitian Notebook* (No. 15)

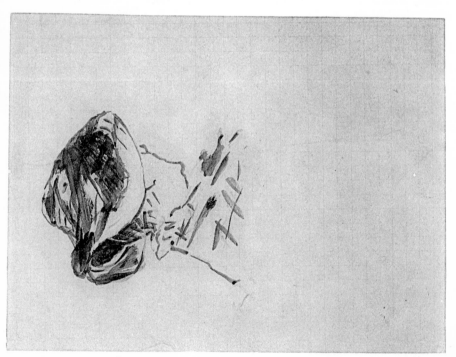

48. Manet   *Mme. Edouard Manet*   49. Manet   *Mme. Jules Guillemet*

50. Lautrec *Study of a Monkey*

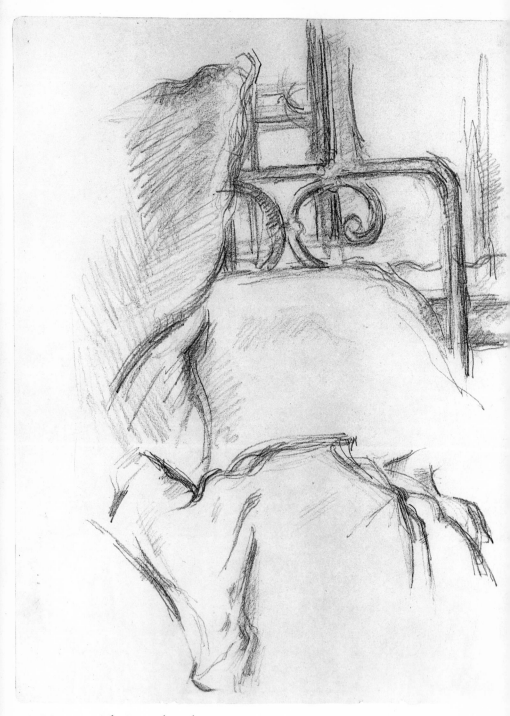

51. Cézanne   *The Unmade Bed*

52. Matisse   *Bust of a Young Woman*

53. Picasso *Sketches of Six Circus Horses, Some with Riders*

54. Picasso   *Two Bearded Men Looking at a Giant Bust of a Woman's Head*

55. German 16th Century *Sketches of German Medieval Castles*

56. School of Manuel-Deutsch *St. Barbara in a Landscape*

57. German or Austrian (?), 18th Century *Music-making Angels*

58. Marcks *Seated Male Youth*

59. Barlach *Two Huntsmen with a Dog, Walking in the Moonlight*

60. Beckmann *Bird Play*

61. Kokoschka *Head and Shoulders of a Woman*